Bright Red Star

Bright Red Star

Story by LI HSIN-TIEN
Illustrations by WANG WEI-HSIN

FOREIGN LANGUAGES PRESS
PEKING 1974

First edition   1974

Printed in the People's Republic of China

I

I was born in Willow Brook Village in the mountains of Kiangsi Province. My parents called me Winter Boy. In 1932, when I was five, I heard grown-ups say they were making revolution. My father, Pan Hsing-yi, was one of those making revolution, and he was a squad leader, too. I was too small to understand what making revolution meant. One day, my father led a band of men armed with swords and red-tasselled spears to the house of Hu Han-san, the local despot who trampled the people of our village underfoot. They dragged the wicked land-lord out, bound him and paraded him in a tall paper hat. Later I heard they divided Hu's land among us poor folk so that we could have land of our own to till and enough to eat. From this I gathered that making revolution meant giving land to the poor and parading the landlord in a tall paper hat.

My father was an ordinary peasant. It was Brother Wu who told him about making revolution.

Brother Wu taught at a school in Bramble Mount, a neighbouring village, but he lived next door to us. One day at noon when I was squatting under a tree at the edge of the field watching father plough, Brother Wu came along. When he saw father sweating at the plough he called, "Knock off a while, Uncle Hsing-yi!"

"I can't," answered my father. "I borrowed this ox and I've got to finish this field before lunch." And he bent again to the plough.

"Stop just a minute, Uncle," urged Brother Wu. "I've got something to tell you."

My father stopped, went up to him and asked, "Well, what is it?"

"We've started a peasants' night school at Bramble Mount. You should go and study there."

"What! Study! Me! Oh, no!" My father returned to his plough. "I can't even feed my family, how can I go to school?"

Brother Wu took father by the arm. "This isn't a school where you just learn to read. We'll hear about current affairs as well. Why not go? There's a lot for us peasants to learn there."

Father pricked up his ears. "Can we learn how to put an end to our suffering?" he asked.

"That's what the school's for." Brother Wu flung out both hands. "To help peasants and workers stand up and change the world."

"It's time we had a change." Father straightened up and mopped the sweat from his brow. Then he continued, his voice strong now. "We work the land, but we have no oxen to pull the plough, no means to repair our houses. Before each May the green crops in the fields are already mortgaged to the landlord. Things can't go on like this."

"You're right there," agreed Brother Wu. "Comrade Mao Tsetung has sent a man here. We should follow the example of the folk on the other side of South Mountain — overthrow the local despots and divide up the land. Better go to the school this evening."

At the mention of Comrade Mao Tsetung, my father's face lit up. "I'll be there," he promised, and went back to his plough.

That evening my father and Brother Wu went to the night school together, and my father went every evening after that. Soon he learned a great deal about revolution and was able to explain it to others. He also learned how to use a broadsword and shoot a rifle. Before long he organized a squad of Red Guards in our village, of which he was chosen squad leader. Thus he led the poor peasants to overthrow the local despots and divide up the land.

After becoming a Red Guard squad leader, my father was quite a different person. And my mother smiled all the time, happy to help my father in every way. She became very busy, and I always wanted to go with

3

her on her errands. Sometimes she would say, "You stick to me like my shadow. Go and look for Sprig next door!" Sprig was Brother Wu's young nephew. He was my age and we often played together.

One day when mother was out organizing some women to make shoes for the army, I went to play with Sprig again. The two of us began singing this song which we had learned from the grown-ups:

> Bright and red rises the sun,
> Comrade Mao has come
> To the Chingkang Mountains,
> Leading the workers and peasants
> To make revolution.
> The poor working people have stood up —
> Down with the despots!
> Share out the land!
> Today every face wears a smile.

The song reminded me of the landlord Hu Han-san being paraded in a tall paper hat.

"You be a landlord," I told Sprig. "I'll tie you up and parade you through the village."

"Let me tie *you* up and I'll parade you instead," said Sprig.

"No, you be the landlord. I'll fetch a rope," I insisted. I ran indoors for a rope and grabbed my friend's arm.

"I won't be a landlord, I won't!" protested Sprig. He tugged at one end of the rope and was trying to tie me up with it when I gave a shove which sent him sprawling. He burst out crying and went off home calling "Ma!"

4

I was in the wrong, I knew. Father always told me never to bully other children. And just then father appeared on the scene, dried Sprig's tears and asked him what was the matter.

"He wants me to be a landlord, and I won't!" sniffed Sprig. Father chuckled and picked up Sprig. "Why won't you be a landlord?"

"Landlords are bad," replied Sprig.

"Quite right. Landlords are no good." Father laughed.

Just then along came Brother Wu, looking very serious. "Hu Han-san has given us the slip," he said to father.

"Scrammed, has he?" Father's eyes flashed. He put Sprig down and drew his Mauser pistol. "Where has he gone? I'll fetch the swine back."

Brother Wu shook his head. "He must have sneaked out in the night. May be in the county town by now."

Father stamped his foot in fury. "If he gets away, that won't be good for us."

I got the general idea of what father meant. Landlord Hu had several hundred *mu* of land and enough grain stored in his house, all grown by the poor, to last his whole household a lifetime. And one of his sons was in the White guards. Landlord Hu was the worst despot around. They should have shot him the day they paraded him. How could they let him get away?

"We were too damn careless," admitted Brother Wu. "Now we've let a wolf escape."

Father clicked the safety catch of his gun. "Never mind where he's gone, I'll fetch him back," he swore, and started off.

"There's no time for that," said Brother Wu, catching father by the arm. "The Whites are attacking Peng Ridge. The superior command asks our Red Guards to intercept the enemy at Cassia Brook." He handed father the order.

"Very good," said father after reading it. "We'll set out right away." And he made straight for the Red Guards headquarters.

We could hear the sound of gunfire at Peng Ridge from our village. When I heard a shot I would ask mother, "Did father fire that?"

Mother would nod and say, "Yes," and I would become very happy, thinking to myself: Dad must be killing a lot of those White guards.

Mother was especially busy the next two days, helping the village women nurse the wounded Red Army men from the front. She fed and tended them and did not return home at night.

On the third morning mother and I were eating breakfast when in came Third Aunt Wu and whispered something into mother's ear, at which mother put down her rice bowl and hurried out. I followed her straight to Landlord Hu's compound and into the east wing of the big house. Father was lying there on a door that had been taken down and used as a makeshift bed. At the sight of us, he sat up. We thought he looked very thin and pale.

"Are you badly hurt?" mother asked him anxiously.

"It's nothing much. A bullet in my left leg." Father turned over, crooking his injured leg. At the sight of his trouser-leg stained with blood, I began to cry.

"What's there to cry about?" scolded my father.

I tried to stop, but couldn't. So I nestled close to mother to muffle my sobs. As mother gently rolled up father's trouser-leg, I saw that the bandage beneath it was dark with blood too. A Red Army doctor came and helped mother remove the bandage to examine the wound.

"We must take the bullet out, Squad Leader Pan," said the doctor.

"Yes, do," father grinned. "It's no use to me there."

The doctor had swabbed out the wound, preparing to extract the bullet, when another wounded man was carried into the adjoining room. Hearing the patient groan, the doctor went out to have a look. When he came back and father asked him what had happened, he told father that one of his comrades had been wounded and needed surgery.

"Can't you give him a shot for the pain?" father asked.

The doctor shook his head. "We've only one ampoule left." He held up the ampoule, meaning to give father the injection.

Father stopped him. "My wound's only a scratch and I don't need it. Give it to him."

Another groan from the next room made the doctor hesitate. "But your operation will take longer than his, Squad Leader Pan," he explained. "You need an analgesic more than he does."

7

"I'm strong as an ox," replied father, "and can stand it no matter how long it takes. Give him the shot. Quick!"

The doctor glanced at mother, who said nothing but turned her face away.

"Tell the doctor to give it to him," said father to mother. Mother looked at father, then nodded to the doctor. "Give it to the other comrade."

So the wounded man in the next room was given the shot, and his groaning soon ceased. When the doctor returned, father said to mother, "Take Winter Boy out."

Mother led me into the courtyard, under a locust tree. Mother told me to stay there, while she hurried back inside. I dared not disobey her but I wanted to have a look, so I sidled back to the door, which had been left ajar. I saw the doctor trying to extract the bullet from father's leg. Blood dripped from the wound and great beads of sweat coursed down father's face. His teeth were clenched and he was breathing hard, but not a sound did he make. I wanted to cry, but father gave me a look that forbade it. Then he beckoned to me, and as I tiptoed forward I heard the clink of metal into an enamel pan. Father asked with a laugh, "Got it out?"

"It's out!" The doctor gripped father's hand. "You're tough all right, Squad Leader Pan. You never once murmured or winced."

"Let me have the bullet," said father.

The doctor picked up the bullet to wipe it off.

"Don't clean it," said father. "I want it with the blood on."

So the doctor put the gory bullet into father's hand, dressed his wound and left.

Father asked mother to place me beside him. Then he put the bullet on the palm of my hand. "Do you know where this bullet came from, son?" he asked.

"From the White guards' guns," I answered.

Father looked at the bullet and then at me. "The White guards have shed too much of our blood. What should we do about it?"

"Get guns and do the same to them."

"That's right," said father, patting my head. "Remember that when you grow up, and if any of those White guards are still around, you must go on fighting them."

I held the bullet carefully, committing his words to memory. Then I asked, "Did it hurt, Dad, when he took the bullet out?"

"Of course it did," father answered.

"Why didn't you cry then?"

"If I had it would hurt just the same. But I refused to cry and I forgot the pain," was father's answer.

Interesting, I thought. So, if you refuse to feel the pain the pain will stop! Was it really like that? I wondered. Mother said I was bothering father too much and led me away. "Don't ask so many questions. Let Dad rest," she said.

After a short convalescence father was able to get about again. And then Brother Wu came, bringing father his assignment. The Red Army was to leave the revolutionary bases and father was to join the main force of the Red Army and go off with it to fight.*

---

* This means going on the Long March. In October 1933 Chiang Kai-shek launched his fifth counter-revolutionary "encirclement and annihilation" campaign with a million troops against the Red base areas. Owing to the erroneous leadership of Wang Ming's "Left" opportunist line, opposed to Chairman Mao's correct political and military line, the fifth counter "encirclement and annihilation" campaign fought heroically by the Red Army over a year finally failed. In October 1934 the Red Army evacuated the revolutionary base areas, carried out the great strategic shift and began the world-known 25,000-*li* Long March.

Mother became busier than ever, sitting up every evening making shoes. She had already made three pairs, and I was very curious why she made so many.

One night I was awakened by my parents' voices. Father had not been home for several nights. What had brought him back tonight? I heard mother ask, "How long will you be away? When will you come back?"

"Not until we've beaten the Japanese invaders," father replied.

"Let me and Winter Boy go with you. I can do some work too."

"Impossible. This is a long campaign for the regular army. Marching and fighting every day."

"When the Red Army is here, our minds are at ease. Once you leave, people won't know where to turn," said mother.

"The Red Army's leaving, but the Party's not. You can go on making revolution." Then, father added, "Of course, with the situation changed, the revolution will have to take a different form."

After another short pause, he continued, "I've spoken to Brother Wu about your joining the Party. He's willing to sponsor you."

"Isn't he leaving?"

"No, he's taking charge of Party work here."

"So long as the Party's here, we shall know where to turn for guidance."

"Once the Red Army goes north, the struggle here will probably become much harder, much more bitter," warned father. "You'll need plenty of grit."

"I can stick it out, don't worry," was mother's answer. "For over a year I've been longing to join the Party, but I know I'm not up to it."

"To be a Party member you have to make special demands on yourself," father told her firmly. "Once you join the Party, you are a fighter in the vanguard of the proletariat."

"I shall do whatever the Party says," mother promised in a voice vibrant with emotion.

"And then there's Winter Boy. It may be years before I see him again. Be sure to bring him up well."

"Don't worry. I'll see to it that he is well brought up."

"If our Worker-Peasant Democratic Government remains here, send him to the Lenin primary school," said father. And as he moved the oil lamp over to look at me, he murmured, "By the time Winter Boy's my age, life should be really good." I felt his hands on my face — big, rough, sinewy and warm. "When I was his age," he continued, "I never knew times even as good as these. Today we have our Worker-Peasant Democratic Government, our Red Guards, the Communist Party and the Red Army."

"If only you didn't have to leave!" exclaimed mother. "If we could go on like this, it would be fine."

"Oh no, the really good times will come with socialism. And even better times with communism."

"How do you mean better?" asked mother, not knowing exactly what father meant.

"All local despots and bad gentry will be overthrown," said father emphatically. "The poor will be liberated.

12

There will be no exploitation or oppression. Peasants and workers alike will be working for the collective. All who toil will have a good life. All the children will be able to go to school. . . ."

Mother gave an exclamation of delight.

"To win all that," father went on, "we have to fight."

As they talked, I fell asleep again and dreamed I was going to school with a satchel over my shoulder. It was a brick school-house with a tiled roof. There were many other school children with me, all in new clothes. . . .

I awoke in the morning to the sound of gongs and drums. Father and mother were already up. I scrambled into my clothes and hurried out. The threshing ground to the east was thronged with people, the air vibrant with the shouting of slogans. I made my way up front and saw it was a send-off for the Red Army. I looked everywhere for father, but there was no sign of him. Suddenly someone touched my shoulder. It was mother. "Come home quick, son," she said. "Your father is leaving."

I followed mother home and there was father neatly dressed in army uniform. On his back were a kit bag, a woven bamboo hat and the shoes mother had made for him. He lifted me up in his arms and kissed my cheeks. "Dad is off to fight the White guards," he said. "You must be a good boy and do as your mother tells you."

I put my arms round his neck. "Go and fight the White guards, Dad," I cried. "I'll go and fight them too when I grow up."

Father laughed and, hugging me again, put me down. He took a book from the table and handed it to me, saying, "This is a Lenin primary school textbook for you to study, son."

There was a red star, and a hammer and sickle on the cover of the book. "When can I start school, Dad?" I asked.

"When school opens again, mother will take you there."

Father said something to mother in a low voice, and she nodded. Then she put the eggs she had boiled into his kit bag and started out with him. I caught hold of father's jacket and cried, "Come back as soon as you win!"

Father turned to me. After a moment's thought, he tore the red star from his bag and gave it to me. "I'll be gone a long time. If you miss me, look at this red star."

I held the red star tightly, my eyes fixed on father. He gave my head a final pat and then strode to the threshing ground to march off with the Red Army. . . .

II

When my father had been gone a month or more, I asked, "Why doesn't Dad come home?"

"The war isn't over yet," said mother. "He'll come back when the fighting is finished."

Month after month passed. Still there was no sign of my father.

"Is Dad never coming home again?" I wanted to know.

Mother assured me that he would come back.

"When?" I insisted, bursting into tears.

Mother hugged me and told me not to cry. Father would come back after the White forces had been wiped

out. She pointed to South Mountain. "Look! When the flowers bloom again up there, Dad will come home."

"When will that be?"

"In spring."

Let spring come soon!

Because mother had told me that father would come back when the flowers bloomed on South Mountain, I often climbed up there to have a look. One day, standing on the summit, I strained my eyes towards the highway, longing to see men and horses heading our way, with father among them. But instead of troops, the only people in sight were a couple of woodcutters. That highway had once been a busy thoroughfare crowded with people delivering grain to the Red Army, with Red Army soldiers passing by and peasants on their way to the fields. Where had everybody gone?

As I stared into the distance some figures appeared, among them some with guns. I said to myself, "It's the Red Army coming back!" Down I rushed as fast as my legs could carry me. But at the foot of the hill I pulled up short. Those men in grey uniforms didn't look like our soldiers. Red Army men wore octagonal caps; these had round ones. And Red Army caps had red stars on them, while these had some sort of small white badge. My heart jumped into my mouth. These were the Whites! Looking more closely I saw among them the despot Hu Han-san who had been paraded in a tall paper hat. The White guards were back! I ran helter-skelter home.

I found mother packing up. Two bundles lay on the bed.

"The Whites are back, Ma," said I panting. "Hu Han-san too!" What shall we do?"

Mother drew me to her and unpicked the hem of my jacket. Then from under the mat on our bed she took the red star father had left me and sewed it inside.

"What about the bullet?" I asked.

"I've buried it under that tree," said mother pointing to the pomegranate in our yard.

"And how about our school book?"

"It's in there." Mother indicated one of the bundles.

"What shall we do when the Whites come?" I insisted.

"Whoever comes and whatever questions they ask, don't say anything."

I nodded.

When mother had sewn up my jacket she sat down to think. She was on the point of going out when we heard shouts in the yard. It was Hu Han-san at the head of a band of White guards. He swaggered in and pointed his cane at mother.

"Where is your husband?" he demanded.

"He's gone north to fight the Japanese," mother answered coolly, without so much as looking at the landlord.

"Got scared and ran away because I've come back, eh?" Hu glowered.

"Only dirty scoundrels run away." This was the first time I heard mother call anyone names, for wasn't it Hu Han-san who had run away?

The veins on Hu's temples stood out. He ground his teeth and, glaring, caught hold of mother. "Out with it! Where has your man gone?" When mother remained si-

17

lent, he slapped her face. "I've got a big score to settle with your husband," he bellowed.

Mother threw off the landlord's hand and drew herself erect, ignoring him.

Hu's eyes suddenly lit on me, and he made a lunge. "Speak up! Where is your Dad?"

Remembering what mother told me, I said nothing.

Finding me just as stubborn as my mother, the landlord set his jaw, knocked me down and kicked me in the stomach. A groan escaped me, but I did not cry. Scrambling up, I still refused to speak.

Hu Han-san clamped a hand on my head. "Tell me, where has your old man run off to?"

In a flash I raised both my arms and removed the landlord's hand, then sank my teeth into it. He squealed like a stuck pig and tried to break loose. But I only bit harder, hoping to bite off a finger. With the other hand Hu fumbled for his gun, while his underlings mauled me too. Seeing the ugly turn things had taken, mother ordered me to let go and pulled me to her. Blood oozed from Hu Han-san's finger and his face was contorted with pain. He aimed his pistol at me.

Mother stepped swiftly between us. "You devil!" she cried. "Stop bullying my child! If you have any guts, settle your scores with the Red Army."

By this time neighbours had gathered in the yard and, at the sight of the pistol in the landlord's hand, they crowded into the room.

"Don't you dare!" they shouted. "Put that gun down."

"The Red Army hasn't gone far."

"If you hurt that child, you'll pay for it with your life."

That took the wind out of the landlord's sails. Whipping out a handkerchief to bind up his finger, he glanced furtively around, then sneered, "A runaway monk can't take the monastery with him. I'll settle scores with you one by one!" Hu ordered his men to clear a way through the crowd. Then, nursing his hand, he left, his face black as thunder.

Now that Hu Han-san was back, mother and I were ready for the worst. That evening we dug a tunnel under the wall of our back yard, so that in case of emergency we could crawl out. The tunnel exit, well hidden in a clump of bamboo, led into a deep gully. We covered the entrance with a flagstone, over which we scattered straw.

A few days went by with no sign of the landlord. Mother often slipped out after dusk and would not return until near dawn. I asked her once where she went.

"What grown-ups do is no business of yours, so don't ask," she told me. "I haven't been anywhere, understand? Now go to sleep like a good boy." After that I knew it was no use asking.

Hu Han-san's return completely changed Willow Brook Village. The Red Guards had gone into the mountains, while thugs from the White "peace preservation corps" loafed about in the streets. We no longer had a village worker-peasant democratic government; Hu became the "corps commander." He ordered his men to paint over the slogans written on the walls by the Red Army before leaving the village and write their slanders over them. The villagers no longer sang or shouted slogans in the streets, and all the bright red flags were hidden away. Even the weather grew dull and overcast.

I began to miss father and the Red Army more than ever and wished they would come back quickly to beat the Whites. After the lunar New Year I longed for the spring when the flowers would bloom again. One evening I climbed up South Mountain to see if there were any flowers. But there were none. I closed my eyes, hoping wishfully that when I opened them again the flowers would be there. Suddenly a voice from behind me called my name. I opened my eyes to see who it was. There stood a woodcutter, and when he shoved back his bamboo hat I saw with delight that it was Brother Wu.

"Is your mother at home?" he asked.

I told him she was.

"Tell her I'll go to see her around midnight. When she hears three knocks on the door, she can open it."

"All right," I nodded. "But when will my father be back?"

"He's fighting a long way from here."

"Hu Han-san's come back."

Brother Wu ruffled my hair, his eyes on our village, now deathly quiet. After a pause, he said, "They can't stay long." Then, catching sight of someone down the hill, he lowered his voice. "Remember what I just told you. Go back and give your mother my message. But don't breathe a word to anyone else."

With that he turned and went up the mountain.

After he had disappeared, I ran home to tell mother. Her face lit up for the first time since Hu Han-san's return. That evening after I was in bed she sat down beside me to wait. She shaded our little oil lamp with a basket so that no light could be seen outside.

I was dreaming, when I heard the murmur of voices. Knowing of Brother Wu's intended visit, I opened my eyes and saw him there by the flickering oil lamp, talking to mother.

Brother Wu was saying that the Red Army had gone north to fight the Japanese and wouldn't be back for some time. "That means those of us here must shoulder a very heavy load. How's the situation in the village?"

"Hu Han-san's trying to organize an armed band," said mother. "He's demanding grain, guns and men, but none of the villagers are co-operating. I called on several families last evening and all would rather die than give that devil grain and guns or manpower."

"That's the spirit," said Brother Wu. "We must organize the revolutionary masses to resist to the end." Then after a pause he continued, "Our Party branch has approved your application for Party membership. From now on you'll be a Party fighter in this village. You must lead the struggle against the enemy."

Mother gripped Brother Wu's hand and answered steadily, "I shall obey the Party in everything. Whatever tasks the Party gives me I shall carry out."

"Now make your pledge."

And so, in the stillness of the night, their shadows, with their fists raised and looming so large, were cast on the wall. I felt it a very special moment and dared not make a sound, though I felt a great warmth surge over me. I seemed suddenly to understand much more about making revolution, that the revolution was carried forward with such Communists as vanguard. Like Brother Wu and mother, they worked day and night, holding mass meetings, leading troops in all weathers to fight the White guards — their whole heart devoted to the poor and oppressed. They would never show the slightest weakness before the enemy but were resolute, for they had made their pledge. When would I be like them and make my pledge?

They talked for a while about how to lead the mass struggle. Then mother asked, "Do you know where Winter Boy's father is now?"

"They've already reached Szechuan." Then, with unusual emphasis he continued, "During the Long March the

Party Central Committee held a conference at Tsunyi. They've corrected the wrong "Left" line and established Chairman Mao Tsetung's leadership in the Central Committee. Under Chairman Mao's command the Red Army has won many victories. It's no longer on the defensive."

"Chairman Mao is our very best leader!" exclaimed mother.

Suddenly there was the barking of dogs outside and mother at once blew out the lamp. We listened intently. The sound of footsteps was growing louder. Mother came over and shook me, and I was up in a flash. Someone was pounding on our gate. Mother thrust a bundle at me, picked me up in one arm and with the other hand led Brother Wu to the back yard. She put me down at the entrance to our tunnel, cleared away the straw, raised the stone and whispered, "Go, quickly!"

When Brother Wu had gotten through the tunnel, mother pushed me in and was getting in herself when the thunderous battering on the gate made her draw back again.

"What are you waiting for?" demanded Brother Wu anxiously from outside the wall.

"It's no good," said mother. "The enemy will find us. Take Winter Boy and escape through the gully. Quick!"

"But you can't stay here!" said Brother Wu. Our gate was still being furiously battered. Mother lowered her jacket into the tunnel saying, "Put this over Winter Boy. Now go!" She replaced the stone and straw over the tunnel entrance and went to the front yard.

I heard the gate give way. What would happen to mother? I was scared stiff, but could do nothing.

"Why didn't you open up?" came a loud bellow.

My heart beat violently. If only mother had come with us!

"What visitors have you had?" The voice was all too familiar.

There was no answer.

"Where's your boy?"

Still no answer.

"The little bastard bit me," went on the voice. "Today I've come to knock his teeth out."

The bellowing voice was that of Hu Han-san.

"Out with it! Where have you hidden that man? Where's your boy?"

Still mother said nothing.

The thugs must have seized mother. I wanted to climb back through the tunnel but Brother Wu held me back and whispered, "Don't move!" Having hidden me behind a rock, he drew his pistol and then sprang nimbly onto the wall.

"Since she won't talk, search the place!" yelled Hu Han-san.

Straw rustled as Hu's thugs searched the yard. I was on tenterhooks when Brother Wu fired, first one shot then three more. From the top of the wall Brother Wu cried, "Squad one, on the left! Squad two, on the right! Close in!"

During the rush which ensued, Brother Wu fired two more shots. I was thoroughly bewildered for I thought he had come alone. Where had these two squads sprung from? Brother Wu jumped down from the wall. At the same time mother emerged from the tunnel.

"You've scared the whole pack away!" she exclaimed.

"Let's go. Quick!" Brother Wu lifted me onto his back and he and mother escaped through the bamboo grove up the gully.

Towards daybreak we reached a forest deep in the mountains. Then I saw the familiar faces of the Red Guards from our village, as well as many people whom I didn't know. I asked Brother Wu what they were doing up there.

"We're guerrilla fighters," he told me.

Tired as I was after all the excitement of the night, I went to sleep as soon as they laid me down in a cave.

When I woke I found my head pillowed on the bundle we had brought from home, with my mother's jacket spread over me. I rolled over and called out for mother, but I was alone in the cave. I got up and went out. All round were tall trees, under one of which Brother Wu was talking with some Red Guards, and mother.

"The enemy is organizing counter-revolutionary armed units in all the villages," said Brother Wu. "They intend to use these forces to wipe us out. So we must mobilize the masses to struggle against Hu Han-san and the other Whites, deny them the grain, guns and manpower they want. Nothing for the enemy! Some comrades must go to Bramble Mount, Willow Brook and Peng Ridge." And he assigned men to each of these villages.

"Let me go to Willow Brook," mother volunteered. "I know the people there."

"You've been up all night and must rest," Brother Wu protested.

"It'll be better to have more comrades, and I don't need to rest. Let me go," mother insisted.

Brother Wu agreed, then said to a man beside him, "Comrade Chen Chun, you take Winter Boy's mother to Willow Brook. Go in after dark and leave before it's light." Wu handed Chen a hand grenade which he fastened to his belt.

Mother came over to me and said, "I've a job to do now, Winter Boy, but I'll be back tomorrow. Mind you don't run wild while I'm gone." Then she and Comrade Chen Chun started down the mountain.

Mother did not come back the next morning. At noon I went and sat on a boulder staring in the direction of Willow Brook Village.

The sun was sinking by the time I finally saw someone coming up the mountain. It was Comrade Chen Chun. "Where's my mother, Uncle?" I asked.

Uncle Chen Chun looked at me without a word, then took me in his arms. He carried me to a big tree where I saw Brother Wu and, still without a word, put me down on a rock and seated himself beside me. Brother Wu looked at Uncle Chen Chun and then at me, and asked, "What happened at Willow Brook?"

Uncle Chen Chun heaved a deep sigh and drew me to him. Tears spilled over from his eyes.

26

"Well, what happened?" repeated Brother Wu.

"They killed the boy's mother."

Shock took my breath away. Then, bursting into tears, I started running down the mountain. Uncle Chen Chun quickly overtook me and asked me where I was going.

"To find Ma."

"It's no use, Winter Boy."

I broke down in a fit of sobbing.

Uncle Chen Chun led me back and sat me down on the rock. Brother Wu asked for the whole story of what had happened.

"When we went to the village last night Winter Boy's mother and I called on several families," Uncle Chen Chun related. "We explained to the people how our struggle was going on, and they were all eager to fight Hu Han-san. After midnight we were about to leave the last house when we were spotted by Hu Han-san and his thugs, who swarmed around us. I threw that hand grenade, the only one we had, and ran. But they pursued us out of the village. We came to a brook and the boy's mother pushed me to safety down the bank, while she crouched there throwing stones at the thugs to draw their attention from me. I told her to run, but she cried, 'Follow the brook. You must go back and report! Don't mind me!'

"What was I to do! She started running, picking up stones and calling out to keep the attention of the Whites. They all chased after her. . . .

"I didn't come straight back," went on Uncle Chen Chun, "but returned to Willow Brook Village at dawn to find out what happened to her. There I heard people say that Winter Boy's mother behaved as a true Communist. She didn't divulge a thing. When Hu Han-san saw he couldn't make her talk he strung her up on a tree and stacked brushwood beneath to burn her to death. The villagers were furious and rushed to her rescue, but that devil Hu posted his armed thugs all round to keep them away. On seeing the villagers, the mother called out, 'Don't be afraid, good neighbours. Time's running out for the Whites. The Red Army will soon be back. Don't believe Hu Han-san's lies. Don't give them any grain. Don't join the peace preservation corps. . . .' Then those devils set fire to the brushwood under the tree. . . ." Uncle Chen Chun broke down here, unable to go on.

I could see in my mind that blazing fire and, in its midst, my mother, her fearless eyes flashing. She was pointing with one finger at Hu Han-san, shrivelled with fear, while her other hand was raised and clenched in a fist, just as I had seen it only two nights before when she pledged her word. I could see the flames leaping brighter and higher, and mother casting a red glow on everything around.

III

I gave the guerrillas a lot of extra trouble. On marches, Uncle Chen Chun carried me on his back. When he was tired, another man would take over.

One day Brother Wu returned from the valley with an old man. He called me to him and said, "I've found a home for you, my boy." I looked at him, then at the old man, whose face wrinkled into a smile. Brother Wu explained that this was Uncle Sung, that he was going to take me home to the valley with him.

"I won't go!" I cried, tears welling up in my eyes. Since mother's death Brother Wu had cared for me like a father. The guerrilla unit had become my home. I couldn't bear to leave. Brother Wu drew me to him and, stroking my head, explained, "We'll be fighting and making forced marches. You're still small, and it's not safe for you here. Go with Uncle Sung. He will take good care of you. And I promise to come to see you whenever I can."

"When I grow up, I'm going to avenge Ma," I declared. "But how can I if I leave you?"

"It'll be years before you're big enough. We'll avenge your mother for you. When you've grown up, we'll come and fetch you."

As I pressed close to Brother Wu, clutching his jacket, Uncle Sung came up to me. "You mustn't be obstinate, my boy," he said. "They'll be fighting every day. Carrying you along would hold them up."

I looked into Uncle Sung's face. It was a very kind face. He took my hand and pulled me to him. His hand was big and warm, just like father's.

Brother Wu fetched the jacket and the bundle mother had given me, and handed them to Uncle Sung. "This is asking a lot of you, Comrade Sung," he said. "But this child is the son of revolutionaries and we must take good care of him."

"Don't you worry, Secretary Wu," replied Uncle Sung. "So long as I live, I promise to bring the boy up for the revolution." He picked up the bundle, placed mother's jacket on my shoulders and took my hand. "Well, my boy, let's be going."

Brother Wu, Uncle Chen Chun and quite a few of the others saw us a good way down the mountain. At a fold in the hills, Brother Wu shook Uncle Sung's hand and said, "This boy's a bud on the tree of revolution, Comrade. You'll look after him well."

"That I will," promised Uncle Sung. "You can trust me."

Brother Wu patted my head again and said, "Go along now with Uncle Sung."

As I said goodbye to the guerrillas, I looked back wistfully at the mountains. Then Uncle Sung thought I might be tired, so he lifted me on his back and we went on our way.

Uncle Sung lived all alone in a cottage in a small village at the foot of the mountains. He told his neighbours that a poor refugee had asked him to take care of me and that he had adopted me. I was to call him uncle. After that I lived with Uncle Sung.

When the weather became warm, I remembered what mother told me — that when the flowers blossomed again on South Mountain, father would come back. So when the grass turned green on the mountain, I would climb up to wait for father. There were no blossoms yet, but some wild grass which would flower had already leafed out. The flowers should soon follow!

One day when Uncle and I were cutting firewood in the hills, I saw a yellow flower by a boulder. Its eight petals, unfurling towards the sun, were a lovely gleaming gold. I gave an excited whoop: "Dad will soon be back!" Then I explained to Uncle Sung, "See this blossom, uncle? Mother told me that when the flowers bloomed on South Mountain, Dad would come back again with the Red Army." I scrambled onto a rock to see the road below. Uncle Sung also sat a while on the boulder.

Finally Uncle Sung said to me, "Time to go home, my boy."

But I would not budge or take my eyes off the road till it was dark and the road could no longer be seen. Then Uncle Sung came, lifted me down and kissed me on the cheek. Only then did we go home.

I was up at dawn the next day, urging Uncle Sung to go to the hills and gather firewood. More flowers had appeared overnight — red, white and yellow — and my delight knew no bounds. Any day now my father would be back with the Red Army to avenge my mother, capture Hu Han-san, parade him through the village in a tall paper hat and then shoot him. I couldn't resist ripping open the hem of my jacket and taking out the red star. It glowed brilliantly in the sunlight, bright and lovely as any red flower. Uncle led me up and we sat a while on a crag. He took the red star from my hand to examine it and, stroking my head, said, "What a day it'll be, my boy, when you can wear a red star like this on your cap."

"I'll sew it on my cap when Dad comes back," I told him. Uncle nodded. Then he asked me to sew it inside my jacket again when I got home. Why bother? I thought, since Dad would be coming back now and I'd be wearing it.

The two of us sat on that crag till almost sunset when Uncle Sung stood up and fixed his eyes on the hilltop. There stood a tall, stately pine with shining, dark green, thick needles. Pointing at the pine, Uncle Sung asked me, "Isn't that a fine, tall pine, my boy?"

"Yes, very," I agreed.

"And sturdy?"

"Yes."

"The pine is an admirable tree," continued Uncle Sung. "It weathers freezing winter winds and the scorching summer sun. Have you ever seen it yield?"

"No!"

"Right, my boy. And we should be as sturdy as the pine, remain ever fresh and green."

I wasn't too clear what Uncle Sung meant, but I nodded just the same.

"Now that the Red Army's gone," Uncle Sung went on, "and the Whites are on the rampage, things are going to be tough for us. But that doesn't scare us. We must be like that pine. No matter how high the wind or how fierce the storm, we won't submit or bow our heads."

I looked up at him. With his wrinkled bronzed face and flashing determined eyes, he really was like the pine on that mountain peak!

"It's not enough just to remember what your mother told you, my boy," continued Uncle Sung. "You must have her courage."

I nodded again, taking in his words. True, my mother had great strength of character. She, too, was like the pine.

"The Red Army won't come back till the Japanese are defeated," said Uncle Sung after a pause. "But no matter how long that takes, my boy, never forget your Dad in the Red Army, that you are the son of a Red Army man."

My heart warmed at these words. I was determined to follow in my father's footsteps to make revolution, just as he had joined the Red Army for that cause. And then I recalled my mother's last words: "Time's running out for the Whites. The Red Army will soon be back." I was sure the Red Army would come back, and my father with it.

Winter came.

One evening when the north wind howled and snow fell thick and fast, I was sitting under the oil lamp reading the schoolbook father left me. Uncle Sung, who had learned to read a little when he was a boy, sat beside me prompting me with the words I didn't know and, telling his own experience in revolutionary struggle to illustrate, explained the lesson to me. This made me understand better what was said in the schoolbook. I still remember distinctly the following verse in it:

> *Workers and peasants,*
> *Never forget:*
> *Without guns*
> *We are helpless as lambs;*
> *To stand up*
> *And win freedom*
> *We must take up arms!*

I pored over the schoolbook until it was time to go to bed and, as I dropped off to sleep, the words, "To stand up and win freedom we must take up arms" still rang in my ears.

I had a dream. I dreamt I had gone back to the guerrillas. So many men and women there waiting to be given arms! I went to stand in line too, but I was only given a red-tasselled spear. That wasn't bad, though, I thought. I could carry it with me wherever I went. Suddenly I heard the shouting of slogans. And what did I see? It was Hu Han-san, the landlord, being paraded in the village streets! How could I let him get away? I rushed forward to strike him with my spear. Then I felt someone

35

restraining my hand. I struggled to free it, and in doing so, I woke up. Why, the room was full of people, and Secretary Wu was stroking my arm! I sat up abruptly and grabbed hold of him. Then I jumped to my feet.

"Winter Boy!" they greeted me. Why, the guerrillas had come back!

"What are you doing here?" I asked.

"We just dropped in while passing through," said Brother Wu.

"We've had another victory," Uncle Sung told me. "They raided the Whites' lair in South Mountain and captured more than twenty guns."

"Give me one," I begged excitedly. "I keep dreaming I had a gun."

The room was filled with laughter.

"So you dream of a gun — fine!" said Brother Wu. "But you're still too small to carry one. Hurry up and grow." And there was more laughter.

Many neighbours came to welcome the guerrillas, whom they considered as their own sons. What warmth pervaded the room! Presently Third Aunt Liu came with six pairs of sandals which she had made of hemp and bits of cloth.

"Here, Secretary Wu, take these," she said.

"Why, Third Aunt," said Secretary Wu, grabbing her hand, "thank you!"

"Don't thank me," replied Aunt Liu. "It's all in the family."

"We happen to be short of sandals," said Brother Wu, drawing a silver dollar from his pocket. "Please take this, Third Aunt."

Third Aunt was taken aback and felt hurt. "I didn't buy these sandals," she protested. "I made them from odds and ends of cloth I saved. The way you keep marching here and there is hard on shoes, I know."

I saw that everyone was moved. Brother Wu pressed the dollar into the old woman's hand, which he clasped in both his own. "I understand your feeling," he said. "But you know our army regulations, Third Aunt. Chairman Mao teaches us not to take a single needle or piece of thread from the masses."

"The idea!" Third Aunt put her other hand over his. "Who are you calling 'the masses'? The guerrilla fighters are one family with us, only you're up in the mountains and we're down in the valley." With that she returned the coin to Brother Wu, telling him to use it for the revolution.

The others in the room all had their opinions. The guerrillas urged Third Aunt to take the money, while the villagers backed her up in her refusal. Brother Wu finally had to put the dollar back into his pocket.

More neighbours packed the room, all crowding around Brother Wu, asking him to tell them how the struggle was going.

Uncle Sung put a jacket over my shoulders and said, "You go out and keep watch. If you see any strangers lurking about, clap three times under the back window." I felt as if I were a sentry on duty and gladly ran out.

The wind had died down; the snow had stopped. Lights still shone from some of the thatched huts. Inside, I thought, the guerrillas must be telling about the ongoing

struggle; and there must be villagers, too, like Third
Aunt Liu who saved bits of cloth to make sandals for
them.   Why did the masses take the guerrillas as their
own? Because the guerrillas love and care for the masses!
I answered my own question.

Presently a guerrilla emerged from the village and went
into our house, and the next moment Brother Wu and the
other guerrillas came out, followed by the villagers.

"Are you leaving so soon?" I asked Brother Wu.

"We must be on our way." He stroked my head. "Be
a good boy and do as Uncle Sung tells you."

I nodded and took his hand. We saw the guerrillas all
the way out of the village.

When Uncle Sung and I came back home, we discovered under the oil lamp a note, and inside it the silver dollar. Uncle Sung held the note up to the light, and by
craning my neck I could read what was written on it:
"Ask Third Aunt to accept this money. Thanks."

Uncle Sung was deeply moved. With me at his heels,
he took the money and the slip of paper to Third Aunt Liu.
When he passed on the message, she held the bright
silver dollar up thoughtfully.

"Very well," she said at last. "I'll buy hemp with this
dollar and save more scraps of cloth to make them more
sandals."

Uncle Sung nodded and, taking from his pocket some
money he had just received for firewood, said, "Take
this too. Buy a little more hemp to make a few extra
pairs."

The old folk's behaviour impressed me. How I wished I too had something to contribute! I made up my mind then and there that when I was big enough I would join the guerrillas and give all I have.

But growing up was a slow process. Spring succeeded spring. By the sixth, when I was thirteen, I asked Uncle Sung more insistently to take me up the mountain to find the guerrillas, but he only shook his head. Uncle Chen had been down several times and so had Brother Wu, but they refused to take me back with them, saying I was still too young.

One day I repeated my request to Uncle Sung. I was a lad now, old enough to avenge mother. But Uncle Sung shook his head as usual saying, "Don't be impatient. You'll be a guerrilla some day, my boy, but not yet. When the time comes, Secretary Wu will send for you." It had been more than a year since Brother Wu, or Secretary Wu, as I came to address him now, had been to see us. We did not even know where he was.

Since Uncle Sung would not take me up the mountain, I decided to find the guerrillas myself. After breakfast I took a rope and carrying pole and, saying that I was off to get firewood, started up the mountain.

When I had crossed two hills, several roads lay before me. I had no idea which of them to take. In order not to lose my way coming back, I chose the widest road, and whenever that forked, I took the wider of the two turnings. Soon I found myself on a ridge, and then in a gully. I dared not ask passers-by the way for fear of disclosing the whereabouts of the guerrillas. But as the

clumps of bamboo and thickets by the path grew denser,
I thought I must be nearing my destination. Before me
now were none but narrow paths, twisting in all directions. It would be all too easy to get lost. I decided to
take a path leading to the summit and stuck twigs beside
the path every few steps to mark the way.

After climbing for some time I halted under a tree which
looked strangely familiar. Why, the cave in front of me
was the one in which I had once slept! And I had been
sitting on that boulder nearby when Uncle Chen Chun
described to me how mother had been burned to death
by Hu Han-san! There was no mistaking the place where
I had cried my eyes out. I ran into the cave. It was empty.
I climbed to a higher place to look around, but there was
no one in sight. Perhaps if I called, someone would hear.
So I shouted at the top of my voice: "Secretary Wu!
Uncle Chen Chun!" But no one answered. Where could
the guerrillas have gone? How I wished I could find
them! How I longed to see those smiling faces and
be taken in as one of them to fight the Whites!

Evidently our guerrillas were off on some mission. I
wouldn't be able to contact them that day. Suddenly my
conscience pricked me. I had not told Uncle Sung where
I was going, and my long absence must be worrying him.
I had better hurry back and search for the guerrillas
some other day. Thanks to the markers I had placed,
I found my way down the road without difficulty. The
sun was already setting, and I began to run.

As I reached a crossroad, I saw some troops approaching. Could this be the guerrillas? I hurried hopefully

towards them. Some of the men had guns and broad-swords, but I didn't recognize any of them. Then I noticed their yellow uniforms — they were White guards! Seeing my rope and carrying pole, they paid no attention to me as they marched uphill. But when the column had almost passed I spotted a man in a long gown and felt hat whose ugly face was familiar. As our glances met, I recognized Hu Han-san! How could I ever forget those wolfish eyes of his! Hate flared in my heart. He looked at me searchingly as he went by. Then suddenly he whirled round.

"Hey, boy, what's your name?" he demanded.

Ignoring his question, I went downhill.

"Halt! Hold on!" he shouted.

I realized that I mustn't stop, and ran faster. There was shouting behind me, and a bullet whizzed past my head. I ran away as fast as I could.

At the edge of the village Uncle Sung was out looking for me.

"Hu Han-san's come. He's after me!" I panted.

Seeing that I was exhausted, Uncle Sung hoisted me onto his back and, after a swift glance up the mountain, quickly carried me home. He gave me two lumps of rice that were waiting on the stove and then led me to the back yard. There he heaved me up onto a tree. "Hurry up! Hide in Third Aunt Liu's yard," he ordered, and from the tree I dropped over the wall. Feeling safe from Hu Han-san's clutches, I breathed more freely. I started to eat my rice.

I had scarcely finished one of the rice lumps when I heard confused sounds coming from Uncle Sung's yard. I listened, then gave a start. Hu Han-san was after me.

"Go on. Tell me where that boy is!" I heard Hu demand.

"He's out gathering firewood," answered Uncle Sung. "He hasn't come back yet."

"That's a lie," retorted Hu. "We trailed him here. And you were seen carrying him back."

"Not me," said Uncle Sung. "I haven't set foot outside the house all evening."

"Stubborn, eh?" Smack! I heard the slap of Hu's hand on Uncle Sung's face. "Come clean now — where did that young bastard come from?"

"A refugee I met on the road gave him to me."

"What's his name?"

"Wang."

"It's not Wang, it's Pan! I'd know that whelp anywhere, even if he was skinned. The young devil bit me!" There followed the sound of another blow. "Where have you hidden him? Speak up!"

"Why should I hide him?" retorted Uncle Sung coolly. "The boy's no thief. He hasn't done anything wrong."

"Is his name Pan, or isn't it?" bellowed Hu.

"His father told me his name was Wang. How could it be Pan? Of course, he can have my name, Sung."

"Don't try to fool me." Hu then gave the order, "Search!"

"What right have you to break in here and search?" I heard Uncle Sung ask Hu indignantly. "You're from

42

Willow Brook. You have no authority here at Mao Ridge."

Hu Han-san gave a mocking laugh. "The whole country's now under the Japanese Imperial Army. I can search anywhere I please."

Hearing that they meant to make a search, I crept into a nook behind Third Aunt's hen-coop.

When the men of the "Imperial Army" failed to find me, Hu Han-san swore at Uncle Sung, "Out with it, you old wretch! Where is young Pan hiding?"

"His name's Wang. He went out cutting firewood and isn't back yet."

"Hand over the boy, or we'll arrest you instead!"

"Why should you arrest me? I'm an honest citizen."

"You conceal bandits."

"What bandits? I don't understand."

"To tell you plainly, old man," Hu shouted, "we've come to the mountains to suppress bandits, and one of them has fled to your place. If you don't hand him over, we'll hand *you* over to the Japanese Imperial Army."

"The boy you're looking for has gone!" Uncle said in a loud voice.

"Gone? Where to?"

"You said you trailed him down the hill. How could I know where you've driven him to?"

"If he's run away, *you* won't!"

I heard the sound of scuffling and the thud of steps. Were they really arresting Uncle Sung? I tiptoed back to the wall, got a foothold on it, and parted the leaves to have a look. They were actually dragging Uncle Sung off! I broke into a sweat. What could I do to save him? Just then Hu Han-san halted and threatened, "Hand over that boy! If we take you off, you're done for."

Scorning even to look at him, Uncle Sung answered curtly, "The boy's gone. You won't be able to find him!" I saw Uncle Sung standing with his head up, without wincing, looking very much like that stately pine on the mountain!

When Hu saw that his ruse had failed, he struck Uncle Sung with his cane and shouted, "Take him away!"

I was on the point of jumping over the wall when Third Aunt Liu came up and caught hold of me.

"You mustn't, Winter Boy," she whispered. "You'd only make things worse for Uncle Sung."

I bit my lips, my heart seeming ready to burst. For six years Uncle Sung had looked after me, and today, in order to save my life, he was taken away just like that. I made up my mind to find Brother Wu and rescue him.

IV

The following evening, Uncle Chen Chun came. He told me Uncle Sung was locked up in a big prison in town.

"Where's the prison?" I asked. "I want to go and see him."

"You can't go there. That's where the Whites jail good people," he answered.

"We can't leave Uncle Sung there. We must hurry up and rescue him."

"Don't worry," said Uncle Chen Chun. "Secretary Wu will find some way to get him out. The Japanese imperialists have invaded these parts, and Hu Han-san's lot are acting as their flunkeys," he added.

"So the Whites have surrendered to the enemy and turned into their running dogs." I began to understand things better.

Finally Uncle Chen Chun told me to wait for Secretary Wu at the foot of North Mountain the next evening. Secretary Wu was finding me a place to stay somewhere else.

45

As I was half sick with worry, Uncle Chen Chun stayed with me till midnight.

The next morning I was awakened by the first cockcrow. Unable to go to sleep again, I threw my jacket over my shoulders and sat up. The room was inky black. Leaning back on the bed, I thought of my father. I imagined him carrying a big red flag charging the enemy amid bursts of gunfire.

When the cock crowed the second time I got dressed. The room was still dark, and my thoughts flew to my mother. In my mind's eye I saw her smile at me, and then, throwing back her hair, walk head erect towards the tongues of flame; I saw her raise her fist and heard her shout: "Don't be afraid, good neighbours. Time's running out for the Whites. . . ."

Day was breaking when the cock crowed the third time. I sat down on a stool, thinking of Uncle Sung, my foster-father who had held his head so proudly as the White guards marched him off to prison. . . .

My father, mother and Uncle Sung — they never stooped or bowed their heads at the point of the bayonet. I'd follow in their footsteps. And Brother Wu and our guerrillas — what a hard life they led, climbing mountains, living in caves with perhaps only sweet potatoes to eat. No, I wouldn't cause them any more trouble. I was already thirteen and no longer a child. I'd wait till I was fifteen, then I would be big enough to carry a gun, run fast and fight the Whites and the Japanese together with the guerrillas. While I was thinking these thoughts, all the cocks near and far started crowing. The room grew light, and I set about tidying up things.

I put Uncle Sung's things together in a bamboo box. My own belongings I wrapped into a small bundle. Third Aunt Liu and some neighbours who knew that I was leaving came to see me off, some of them with presents of food. For six years I had lived and grown up among them, and they treated me as one of their own. How could I ever thank them? I said goodbye to them and asked them to keep an eye on the cottage. Then I took a look round the courtyard, locked the gate and, taking the bundle, started up the mountain.

It was spring. The trees on the mountain were green, the bamboos were sprouting new shoots, flowers were in bloom, birds were on the wing, brooks gurgling down every gully. It was a day to take your breath away. If only it was still a Red area, I would have been free as the birds, merry as the fountains. But as it was, Hu Han-san had stretched out his black tentacles to seize me so that I could no longer stay at Uncle Sung's. "Hu Han-san, you White cur!" I swore. "Some day I shall settle scores with the lot of you!"

I lay low all that day in the mountains. Then, as dusk fell and it was time to go to meet Brother Wu, I stood up to take a last look at Uncle Sung's thatched cottage. I wouldn't be able to see Uncle until he came out of prison. The sun was setting, and the air became chill. I opened my bundle and took out mother's old jacket, the sight of it bringing mother closer to me. I fingered the lower hem. When my own jacket had become too small for me, I had sewn my father's red star into the hem of my mother's garment. Now, throwing it over my shoulders, I started down hill.

At the foot of North Mountain I met Brother Wu and Uncle Chen Chun and was so happy to see them that I grabbed Brother Wu's hand and held it tightly in mine for a long, long time. Finally I asked, "Where is my Dad?"

"In Yenan," he told me.

"In Yenan?"

"Yes, they've reached Yenan with Chairman Mao." There was a radiant smile on Brother Wu's face as he mentioned this. "After a long trek of 25,000 *li*," he continued, "your father arrived in Yenan and now he's fighting the Japanese under the command of Chairman Mao."

Immediately scenes appeared in my mind of parading the local despot and dividing up his land, of mass meetings to struggle against the oppressors, of Dad going to join the Red Army on the Long March, of mother making her pledge with her fist raised, and of guerrillas fighting the enemy. . . . "These are all part of the revolution," I said to myself, "carried out under the leadership of Chairman Mao. Chairman Mao also leads the Red Army and the people in fighting the Japanese invaders and in doing many, many other things I do not yet understand. When he was here, red flags were unfurled everywhere, in Willow Brook and Mao Ridge, and the villagers sang. What a wonderful place Yenan must be now!" When I thought of this, I said to Brother Wu, "I also want to go to Yenan to be with Chairman Mao."

Brother Wu laughed, saying, "I want to go too, but not now. It's too far away."

"Where is Yenan, anyway?" I asked.

"In the north."

I turned to look in that direction. It was aglow with radiant clouds. So that was where father was with

Chairman Mao! How I wished I were a bird and could fly there!

"Winter Boy," said Brother Wu after a pause. "Let's talk about things more urgent at present. Hu Han-san is after you; it won't be safe for you to stay here in Mao Ridge. I'm looking for a place for you to stay in town. How about going to a rice shop there as an apprentice?"

"Be an apprentice in town?" I shook my head. "Oh, no, not that!" In these six years when I was staying with Uncle Sung, I had been to town twice. I had seen shop apprentices, all in their early teens, standing behind the counter looking so dull, like birds in cages!

"You'd better go, my boy," urged Brother Wu. "Hu Han-san knows that you're here. You'll have to shift to another place."

"I won't go," I grumbled. "Even if I die here, I'll stay with the guerrillas."

"That won't do, my boy," urged Brother Wu patiently. "Do you know why I want you to be an apprentice? Because you'll be safer that way. We have a comrade in town who can look after you." Seeing me still unwilling to go, he continued, "The Party organization must see to it that a Red Army man's son is well looked after. When you grow up, you can join the fighting ranks."

His words convinced me. I nodded and said I'd go.

The next morning I was taken to town by Uncle Chen Chun, who posed as a pedlar of firewood. We went to see a seal-engraver whose name was Chao. Uncle Chen Chun spoke to him for a while, then left me with him.

I stayed in Uncle Chao's home for two days, and on the third he told me he was to take me to a certain Mao Yuan Rice Shop on South Street where I would be an apprentice. I took my little bundle along. Soon we came to a shop with a three-door frontage where Uncle Chao pointed to a horizontal signboard: Mao Yuan Rice Shop. "Here we are," he announced, and presently I heard a cough. The person who came out was a short fellow with a fat head.

"Proprietor Shen, I've brought you this boy," said Uncle Chao.

The pudgy proprietor looked me over from head to foot. "Very countrified, very countrified indeed," he muttered.

"The boy's a relative of mine from the country," Uncle Chao explained. "But very honest and dependable."

"All right. Come in," Shen said beckoning, and we entered a room behind a door screen. The first thing the man asked Uncle Chao was, "Have you brought the money for the bond?"

Uncle Chao drew a pile of banknotes from his pocket, saying, "This is half of it. The rest will be paid next month," to which Shen nodded.

"But be sure to bring the money early in the month," he added.

"Certainly," replied Chao.

I was greatly puzzled. Why should an apprentice have to give the proprietor money? Before I had hit on an

answer, the man asked me abruptly, "What's your name?"

"Kuo Chen-shan." Fortunately, Chao had told me this was to be my name.

"Any nickname?"

"Winter Boy."

"We'd better call you Winter Boy." Then with a cough he continued, pointing at the pile of banknotes on the table, "See that? From now on you're to work here. Don't take anything that doesn't belong to you. Whatever you steal will be deducted out of that."

I was furious at this fellow's assuming I was a thief. What had I ever stolen?

"You are not to quit the job for three years," he said. "If you do, the bond will be forfeited."

"He won't. The boy can do any kind of hard work. How can he quit?" put in Uncle Chao, forcing a smile.

"If the boy does well, the money will be returned at the end of three years when the contract expires," the shopowner concluded with another cough.

I felt like stamping out of the place that very moment. I thought of Brother Wu and the guerrillas who had so little to eat and wear, and yet they had to hand over such a large sum to this fat man on my account. And Uncle Chao had to deal with this man. I looked at Uncle Chao. He smiled at me, and from his smile I knew that he wanted me to stay. Refusal would put him in a very embarrassing position, so I controlled my feelings and didn't say anything.

The fat proprietor stuffed the money into his pocket and then told me to open my bundle for his inspection. "Now go and see the mistress," he said, coughing again.

Mistress? What was that? I stood there completely dazed.

"Let's go and see her," I heard Uncle Chao say, and followed him reluctantly to the rear quarters.

We passed along a narrow corridor till we came to a compound with rooms on the north, east and west sides and were taken to a room on the east. There was a lanky woman of about thirty, with an elongated face and high cheek-bones, her two big front teeth protruding from her large thin-lipped mouth. Another faded woman of over sixty stooped over a short-handled broom sweeping the floor. There was also a girl of about twelve sitting on a low bench, pale-faced, cross-eyed and with a pointed nose. The girl was sucking a lollipop, now and then showing her decayed teeth. On the middle wall hung a large picture of the God of Wealth, while on the long table in front of it were placed two candle-sticks and an incense burner.

The fat shopowner gave another two coughs before entering the room. "This is your mistress," he said indicating the lanky woman. I looked at her but said nothing, while she only turned away and took a seat at the other end of the room. The next to be introduced was the girl sucking the lollipop. "This is my daughter," said Shen. Again I remained silent, feeling annoyed at these people who were so cold and unpleasant. I thought again of leaving, but when I looked at Uncle Chao he turned to Shen and said, "Will you take the boy to see the other staff members of the shop?"

Proprietor Shen then took me and Uncle Chao into the shop. Six persons were behind the counter: manager Chien, bookkeeper Feng, two shop-assistants, Ma and Chu, and two apprentices, the older one named Wang Kensheng and the other Liu Lai-tzu. Uncle Chao introduced me to them as a new apprentice and asked them to treat me well. When all the arrangements had been made, he left.

I felt dizzy with what I had seen in the rice shop. The paying of money-bond, the searching of my bundle, meeting the so-called mistress — what was it all about? I felt a great weight on me.

Now I was standing behind the counter, with people coming and going. I had never seen so many people in my home village! They came one after another to buy rice, paid for it and left. And so it was, over and over. I did not want to be in anyone's way, so I moved into a corner and stayed there watching.

It was not until darkness fell and the wooden shutters had been put up that I spread my bedding on the floor behind the counter as the other two apprentices did. When I lay down on the hard wooden floor, tears started from my eyes in spite of myself. I yearned for Willow Brook under the Worker-Peasant Democratic Government, where the poor were not oppressed. I recalled what father had said to mother before he went on the Long March, about the good days to come when the poor of the world would be liberated and there would be no oppression or exploitation. . . . Now, right here in this place I was being oppressed and exploited! My heart sank.

Every day in the rice shop I had to wait on the proprietor, the manager and the rest. That tall, skinny woman would often yell at me with her screeching voice as unpleasant as herself, "Winter Boy, go and get me a packet of cigarettes"; "Winter Boy, go and fetch some sweets for my daughter!" It seemed that girl of hers was sucking sweets or munching away at something all day long, and every time she wanted more I was sent to fetch it. Sometimes I felt my anger would burst out. You, too, have legs. Why can't you go yourself? I would be on the verge of shouting back. How I wished people in this town could rise and make revolution as we did in Willow Brook. Let there be revolution! Just see if you could sit at home then and get whatever you want without working!

At the end of my endurance, I went to see Uncle Chao one day. "Please let me go back to my village. I can't get used to life here," I implored.

Uncle Chao smiled at me kindly and asked me to sit beside him. He said, "Hu Han-san is searching for you everywhere. It's not safe to go back." Seeing me not yet convinced, he continued, "You have to stand many unpleasant things in the rice shop, but it's safer there because you don't attract attention."

What Uncle Chao said was true. Hu Han-san certainly would not spare any family member of the Red Army.

56

"You can leave the shop when the time comes," he assured me.

"All I hear every day is how to make money — nothing else," I told Uncle Chao.

"By the way," interrupted Uncle Chao, "don't waste your time in the rice shop." Saying this, he took me to an inner room and gave me a magazine which he took from under his mattress. "Here's an old journal. Take it with you and read it in the evening. You'll find a lot in it about revolution."

This old journal, its cover worn away by much handling, must not be carelessly left about for just anyone to see, I guessed. I put it in an inside pocket. Before I left, Uncle Chao told me again that I could leave the rice shop as soon as the situation was more favourable. And since I considered this as the decision of the Party organization, I went back with the journal without further protest.

I got along very well with the two other apprentices in the rice shop, especially with Liu Lai-tzu who was also from a poor family in a village that had seen revolution. When the three of us spread the gunny bags on the floor for our bed, Wang would fall asleep almost the minute he lay down, but Liu and I would talk. Sometimes, under the dim light, we read the magazine Uncle Chao gave me.

The more we were oppressed, the more we longed for revolution, and our eyes were being opened. We exchanged the little we knew about making revolution. In muffled voices we read earnestly the following lines in the journal:

Think, everybody, think,
Look, everybody, look
At the present state of affairs.
Landlords do no work,
But their barns burst with grain.
Rich people live in idleness,
But they grow fat from too much food.
Workers and peasants toil and sweat,
And never get enough to eat,
Ill clothed,
No roof over their heads.
Think, everybody, think,
Shouldn't things be changed?

The dim light filtered down as, side by side, Liu Lai-tzu and I discussed our life in the rice shop — how we were always ill-treated and browbeaten.

One rainy day I was called by that shrieking, ugly-voiced skeleton of a woman to the back compound. She wanted me to take the chamber pot to be repaired, and at the same time buy some sweets for her daughter. I was drenched when I got back. Then her daughter wanted to go to the toilet and, not wanting to go to the outhouse in the rain, used a wash basin instead. Imagine! That woman ordered me to empty and clean the basin! Indignant, I dashed out of the room and went straight to the shop up front.

I was soaked and shivering with cold. Still, not minding Liu Lai-tzu's advice to change my clothes, I was standing there motionless and dumb when that woman came, shouting and yelling, ready to devour me. She made a scene in front of her husband, who immediately ordered me to empty the basin. I refused. He was about to strike me when the old woman servant came to say that she had done the job. At this news his wife flared up at the old woman. "Who told *you* to empty it? I told *him* to do it. I'll teach him to disobey me!"

The shopowner came over again to strike me, but was prevented by the shop-assistants.

Still that lanky woman would not let me go. She shouted that I must be punished by kneeling. "Never seen an apprentice like him in all my life," she fumed.

"Go over there and kneel down," the shopowner ordered threateningly, "and besides that there'll be no supper for you tonight!"

I was no longer shivering. Angry but self-possessed, I dashed out to the storeroom at the back, where Shen's loud shouts of "kneel down, kneel down" still reached my ears. I paid no attention and, as it was raining hard and the fat proprietor did not wish to get wet, he contented himself with shouting. Finally I banged the door, shutting myself in the storeroom, and that was that.

I stood by the window looking out at the pouring rain and began to feel cold in my wet clothes. Fury and hatred rose within me against them all — the fat proprietor and his lean wife. They ordered me about, insulted me and sought to punish me by making me kneel down, apparently feeling it their right. What kind of life was this? I felt such a shop should be razed to the ground.

V

We longed for revolution. But the high tide of the revolution hadn't yet come to this county seat. We looked forward to the coming of the Red Army, but, according to Uncle Chao, they were fighting the Japanese at the front. Thus, in expectation and longing, I stayed in the rice shop for more than a year. . . .

Another spring. And this spring the days were even harder for the poor. The drought of the previous year affected the rice harvest. In the countryside, the poor peasants had no rice to eat — whatever was harvested was taken away from them. In the cities, the poor had no money to buy rice, for the price soared daily.

But in proprietor Shen's warehouses the sacks of grain were stacked high.

One evening Liu Lai-tzu called me to go to the back door of the shop, which opened on a river. A boat was anchored there. I saw Wang Ken-sheng and another man from the shop unloading gunny bags from the boat, and then taking them inside. Liu Lai-tzu wanted me to help, so the two of us carried one bag between us. It felt especially heavy, far heavier than a bag of rice. "What's in it?" I asked Liu Lai-tzu, feeling it with my hand. Lai-tzu shook his head as though to say don't ask. We carried the heavy bag into the back yard. Several such bags were unloaded and put outside the warehouse. Curious, I opened one of the bags when no one was around and took out a handful of the contents. It was not rice but fine gravel! I asked Liu Lai-tzu what it was for, and he said, "Wait and you'll see."

Ordinarily we apprentices were the last to get off work. That night, however, we were told to turn in early, but I wanted to find out what was happening and stayed awake. After a while, I saw manager Chien and the other two men go to the storeroom. Liu Lai-tzu nudged me and we both got up and crept to a vantage place nearby. There was proprietor Shen and the manager emptying a bag of the gravel onto a pile of rice, while the other two men mixed it in with pitchforks! So that was it! They were weighting the rice with gravel to sell to the people! The blood-sucking proprietor Shen! Weren't you already squeezing enough money out of people? I would have gone nearer for a closer look but Lai-tzu pulled me back

61

and we went back to our pallets to sleep. For a long time I lay awake thinking I couldn't go on working for those heartless creatures!

The next afternoon when I was out buying sweets for Shen's daughter, I went to see Uncle Chao. He was engraving a seal, and when he saw me he got up and we went inside.

"Used to the life in the rice shop yet?" he asked with a smile.

"Oh, no!" I shook my head. "They're always playing dirty tricks."

"What dirty tricks?"

"In the middle of the night they mix gravel into the rice!" Then I told Uncle Chao what happened the night before.

"The landlords and capitalists are the most cruel people in the world. They'll stop at nothing if it benefits them," said Uncle Chao indignantly.

"I won't stay with those bad people any longer," I said. "I won't work in that rice shop any more. Send me to the guerrillas. I'm already fourteen and I won't be a bother any more."

Uncle Chao paced the floor for a while, then shook his head and said, "The revolutionary situation is developing fast now. Most of the guerrillas have gone to the front to fight the Japanese. . . ."

Realizing that my request was impossible to fulfill for the time being, I thought of another way of leaving the rice shop. I said, "Uncle Chao, teach me to engrave seals; I'll learn the trade from you."

"But I'll be leaving this place very soon," answered Uncle Chao with a smile.

"You're going to leave here?"

"Yes. I've accepted a new task. I must go."

"I'll go with you."

"No, I can't take you along," said Uncle Chao, patting my shoulder affectionately. "It's safer for you to stay here. Besides, you can see for yourself what a wicked society we live in. I'll ask you to leave here and join the army when it's possible." Uucle Chao then gave me a pair of shoes. "Take these," he said. "I bought them for you."

I took the shoes. My heart felt warm. In the revolutionary ranks everywhere one found people like in one's own family!

Uncle Chao reached under the mattress on his bed and took out a book, saying, "Here's something else for you to read in your spare time in the evening. Increase your knowledge and learn more about the revolution. It will serve you well in future." I took the book and concealed it under my jacket, thanked Uncle Chao and then returned to the rice shop.

When I got back I heard voices inside. On investigation I saw the police bureau chief Sun talking to Shen. He said, "Proprietor Shen, you've hoarded all this rice and still won't sell. What if the townspeople want rice and can't buy any?"

"I couldn't care less!" retorted Shen. "The quotation on rice is up and I'm waiting for a better price!"

63

"You're engaging in speculation, you know," said the police chief. "And if people know and start a riot, it might be hard to handle."

"Then I'll have to depend on your help. With you for a friend, what have I got to be scared of?" said the fat proprietor, fawning on the police chief with imploring eyes.

"You make a fortune and I'm the middle-man, eh? Ha, ha, ha!"

"I'll not forget you. . . ." With that the proprietor fished out a pile of banknotes and put it into the hand of the police chief. . . . Then both laughed coarsely.

A child's cries came from the shop up front and I hurried there. A woman dressed in rags held a baby in one hand, while in the other was a bamboo basket. Two banknotes of low denomination lay on the counter, and the woman was begging the men behind the counter to sell her some rice. "Please," she said, "just a little. We haven't eaten anything for two days. Have pity on the child. You can see it's crying from hunger." The child, two or perhaps three years old, was weak and emaciated. Its head drooped, too big for the starved body, and its eyes seemed monstrous in its bony little face.

"There's nothing I can do. The rice is sold out, not a grain left," lied manager Chien. "You'd better try at another shop."

But the woman wouldn't leave, and just then out came Shen. Seeing the poor woman with her sobbing child he glared at her and roared, "Why bawl and make such a fuss in my shop? No one has died here. Get out!"

64

"The child is hungry, proprietor. Sell us just a little rice," begged the woman, who was trying at the same time to soothe the child so it wouldn't cry.

"Get out! The rice was all sold long ago." The proprietor brushed the two banknotes onto the floor and strode inside again.

The woman stooped, picked up the money and, staring vacantly at the men behind the counter, slowly walked away, the child still wailing on her arm. The look she gave me with her tear-misted eyes was like two knives thrust into my heart, causing me great anguish.

The woman had gone, but the crying of the child remained in my ears. Certainly it was not pleasant to be hungry, and I silently cursed proprietor Shen for letting people starve while he hoarded rice waiting for a better price!

The less the rice sold, the more were the people who wanted to buy. Every morning when the shutters were taken down long queues of people were already waiting outside the shop. Shen simply ordered us to say "No rice now," which met with angry glances. Some people began to use violent language.

One afternoon we three apprentices were ordered to go to the back door of the shop to carry in another boatload of rice. Liu Lai-tzu and I had just carried in one bag when we heard an uproar up front in the shop. Manager Chien came rushing out to tell us to put up the shutters. We went to the shop front. And oh, the crowd that had gathered there! All were shouting, "Rice! Rice!" Proprietor Shen was there, sweating all over! And the two shop-assistants were gesticulating and shouting at the top of their voices, trying to pacify the rioting crowd. The scene reminded me of those in my home village when we paraded the local despot and then divided up his land, of dashing into the landlord's barns, dragging out the bags of rice and dividing them up among the poor peasants. How I wished these people could also break through the shop front and take the bags of rice away! How I wished they would seize proprietor Shen! I couldn't help laughing as I thought all this!

Smack! The flat of the proprietor's hand came down on my cheek. "What are you laughing at?" he demanded angrily. "Hurry and get the shutters up!" The veins standing out on his forehead, his face livid, he looked like a stuck pig.

I ambled outside where the people were gathered, shouting, "Make way, make way, we're going to put up the shutters."

A ricksha man came up to me and demanded, "Why are you putting up the shutters? The sun hasn't set yet! We want to buy rice!" I told him in an undertone that bags of rice were being unloaded at the back of the shop. Then he shouted, "Hey, Mr. Proprietor, will you sell rice or not?"

"I've no rice."

The man shouted, "Listen, folks! They're unloading bags of rice at the back door of the shop, and yet this proprietor won't sell us a single grain. He wants to starve us. Let's go to the back door." Then he ran for the river landing, and everyone rushed after him.

This struck terror into Shen. "Quick! Go. . . go to the back door . . . and carry the rice in!" Shen's voice was trembling.

"Do I still have to put up the shutters?" I asked deliberately.

"Of course," Shen glared at me.

"Which shall I do first, carry in the rice or put up the shutters?" I asked again.

"Do both at once!" he shouted at me as he rushed towards the back door at the head of the others.

After putting up the shutters I too went to the back. There was a large crowd on the bank of the river, all trying to prevent the rice from being taken in. Shen, who had never lifted a finger to do any work, was today carrying a bag together with manager Chien. Ma and Chu had one too. They were surrounded by a rioting crowd.

"You said there was no rice. What's this?" demanded the ricksha puller.

"Even if there was I wouldn't sell it to you!" retorted the proprietor.

"That's speculation and hoarding!"

"It's none of your business!"

"When you starve us, we have to take things into our hands." Then the ricksha puller turned and shouted to the others, "Come, folks, help yourself!"

The crowd surged forward and someone tried to tear open the bag Shen and Chien were carrying. The proprietor nearly had a fit. They put down the bag and Shen flung himself upon it, shouting and kicking his short

67

legs. "Whoever dares to touch my rice will pay for it with his life!" He made such a scene that again I couldn't help laughing.

Meanwhile, another crowd had boarded the boat and out of spite begun to throw the bags into the river — "splash, splash!" A third splash and the proprietor got up off his bag of rice and yelled for all he was worth, "Whoever throws the rice in the river will have to pay for it!" As Shen made for the boat, the crowd pounced on the unprotected bag of rice, tore it open, and filled their bags and baskets. Then more people came after the bag that Ma and Chu were carrying. Those who could not get at the bags rushed onto the boat. Proprietor Shen rushed about like a chicken with its head cut off. Suddenly someone on the boat shouted, "It's sinking!" Everybody rushed to the bow of the boat; then with a "whoosh" the boat turned upside down.

Bedlam reigned on the bank. Those who could swim jumped into the water to drag out those who had fallen in. Proprietor Shen had also fallen into the river and was thrashing about to get out. Such a sight the fat man was — bobbing up and down, kicking desperately! Suppose he did drown! How many lives had he taken, mixing gravel in the rice, hoarding and speculating! One by one those who had fallen into the river were hauled ashore. But Shen was not among them, for no one had the slightest desire to save him. In the end it was Ma who dragged him out, so swollen with water that he looked like a toad spread out there on the bank.

Everyone had been brought out of the river, but the rice had gone to the bottom! Proprietor Shen just stared at the water like one who'd lost his mind, shouting, "Rice! Rice! Hurry up and salvage it!" Then he shakily made his way home. He whispered something into manager Chien's ear when Chien went to help him, and Chien nodded and went away.

When the two bags of rice had been emptied and the rest was at the bottom of the river, the people once again rushed to the front of the shop. There was the same woman with the baby.

"Isn't it a pity that all that rice has gone to the bottom of the river!" she said to me.

"It doesn't make much difference," said I. "The rice can be salvaged, and it'll only save the proprietor the trouble of weighting it to sell to you." The child was still whimpering; the woman's basket was still empty. I asked her why she didn't get any rice when the two bags were torn open. She said that with the child and the basket she couldn't get through the crowd. "Your proprietor is heartless. He's only out to make money even if he starves people to do it," she added as she walked listlessly towards the front of the shop, with me following.

There was a clamour at the front of the shop with shouting and banging. People were pounding on the closed shutters, and I was again reminded of our attack on Hu Han-san's house. Every knock must have sent a shiver down proprietor Shen's corpulent torso, and his skeleton of a wife scampering to burn incense before her image of the God of Wealth! Soon two young men came along with a heavy wooden pole and with that they began to ram at the shutters! I heard angry voices: "Open the door! Open the door! We want to buy rice! We must eat to live!" The shutters rattled with every thrust of the ram. It looked as though they would give way any moment.

Then there was a shout: "The cops! The cops are coming!" Some twenty policemen, all armed, were led in by manager Chien. The police chief Sun was there too, a pistol tucked in his belt and a dagger in its sheathe dangling at his hip. "Who's the ringleader?" he thundered. "Go away, the lot of you! You're disturbing the peace!" Still nobody budged, and he ordered his men to disperse the crowd. When the policemen had their guns pointed at the crowd, the ricksha puller sprang forward and faced the police chief. "You'd better take the proprietor of the shop to the police station. He's the one — hoarding, speculating, and starving us to death."

"Who are you?" demanded the police chief.

"I'm one of the people who've come to buy rice."

"The rice belongs to the rice shop. It's up to the shop-owner to sell or not. You're creating a disturbance."

"No, we're not. We only want to buy rice. We have to eat, or else we die. All he has to do is open up the shop and sell us rice. That's all."

This argument was interrupted by the opening of a small aperture in one of the shutters through which pro-prietor Shen called out to the police chief: "Arrest that man! He's a robber — brought a mob here to steal my rice!"

"Put this man under arrest!" ordered the police chief.

At this, the ricksha man jumped onto the doorstep and addressed the people. "Listen, folks!" he began. "This man who hoards rice and refuses to sell gets away with it, while we who only ask to buy rice to keep us from starving are accused of lawbreaking. Is that fair?"

"No! It's not fair!" chorused the people.

"You have no right to arrest the ricksha puller. Arrest the proprietor first!"

The police chief only kept on shouting, "Arrest him! Arrest him!"

The crowd was seething and began battering at the shutters again. Two policemen grabbed for the ricksha puller, who shoved one of them to the ground with one

hand. The police chief aimed his gun to shoot. Just then the woman with the child, who was standing beside me, threw her basket down and stepped in front of the police chief, held up her hand and shouted, "Don't shoot! He's a good man." The police chief fired. The bullet hit the child in the head. Blood streamed from that little, pale, bony face, flowing onto its mother's breast and to the pavement in front of the rice shop.

"They're killing us! We must settle accounts with them!" The angry crowd closed in on that police chief, who hid behind the policemen, ordered them to fire, and arrest the ricksha puller. To prevent his being arrested, many men surrounded the ricksha puller while others helped the weeping mother away. . . .

Then the shutters were removed from the rice shop, and the proprietor hurriedly invited the police chief in.

VI

The incident at the rice shop was over. The proprietor lost two bags of rice; a poor woman lost her child. These events were not forgotten, however. The tragic news of the child-killing spread, adding another deep gash of hatred in the people's hearts. The blood on the pavement was soon rubbed away, but it was not erased from people's minds. Every time I passed by I could see that pinched, pale little face with its two huge sunken eyes, and then the child's mother, that poor starving woman weeping over the murdered child, and the ricksha man who led the people to fight for rice. Now I began to see things more clearly. Proprietor Shen and the police chief were of the same lair. Didn't the police chief often go to Shen's home for food and wine, and help Shen whenever he was in trouble? The poor, who had no rice to eat, also joined together and helped each other. The ricksha puller had stepped forward to speak for the people, so that they could have something to eat. And the poor woman sacrificed her child to the police bullet in order to save the ricksha puller. Yes, these two kinds of people travelled two different roads! They were of two classes, just as the poor peasants and the landlords of our village were of two classes.

After the rice incident, Shen had a notice posted on the front door of the shop: "Under repair. Business temporarily suspended." Now we didn't even have to bother taking the shutters down and putting them up again every day. The price of rice was soaring; proprietor Shen was all smiles. "I lost two bags of rice, but ill fortune has brought good in its wake," he gloated. "By closing the shop a few days I'll net the equivalent of a dozen bags!" Shen spent his time entertaining the police chief and other county officials.

One day proprietor Shen prepared an especially big feast, and as I was wondering who he was inviting, the police chief dropped in. "This time," said he to Shen, "I've really brought you a God of Wealth! This man has quite a few hundred *mu* of land which nets him some two thousand piculs of rice a year! Besides, he's the commanding officer of the local Peace Preservation Corps,

73

with over a hundred men under him. He feeds them by public rice collection. If you make friends with him, you've got a bottomless source of rice. Why, you'll make a fortune!"

Proprietor Shen was overjoyed. He bowed and bowed, till I thought he was going to kneel down and kowtow! "It's all due to your kindness. You've brought me good luck. I'll reward you well, give you a feast, ha, ha. . . ." At this point, manager Chien came in to announce that the guest had arrived by boat. Shen became very excited and went with the police chief to the back door of the shop.

I was ordered to clean up the north guest room in the back compound. Ordinarily, guests were received in a room up front, and only special ones were ushered into this inner room favoured with southern exposure. A large round table stood in the middle of the room, which I had rubbed and polished till it shone like a mirror. On the table stood a pot of newly-brewed tea. A plate of melon seeds and another of sweets, plus a large plate of tangerines, were placed around the teapot. Soon I heard footsteps and proprietor Shen and the police chief talking to someone. "This way, please! Come in, please!" uttered Shen in a fawning voice, and the man entered the room. He wore a long gown over yellow woollen riding breeches, a felt hat and black leather shoes. He first quickly searched the room with his gaze. When it fell on me, I saw two wolfish eyes. Could I ever forget those eyes? Why, it was our village despot, Hu Han-san! "So it's you! You skunk. . . !" I cursed under my breath, but

Hu Han-san did not notice me. He was immediately taken to the seat of honour, where I was to serve him with tea, cigarettes and the sweets. When I struck a match to light his cigarette, he looked sharply at me. I turned and left the room.

I went dizzy with what appeared before my eyes — mother strung up on the tree with the flaming brushwood under her and Uncle Sung dragged away and thrown into a dark, damp dungeon; Hu Han-san at the head of a pack of Whites and Japanese soldiers attacking our guerrilla base. . . . And now that very Hu Han-san was sitting in the guest room! I burned with hatred. And as I was thinking how to avenge these wrongs, I heard Hu Han-san say, "Who's the boy that lighted my cigarette just now? Where's he from?"

"This county, just outside the city," answered Shen.

"I see. Looks like someone from my village."

"From your village?"

"Never mind if he's a native of this place."

Just then Liu Lai-tzu came to ask me to help unload rice. "More rice?" I asked in surprise.

"The man who just came brought it."

"How much?"

"A full boatload. Forty to fifty piculs."

"Must have been squeezed from my fellow villagers!"

"How's that?" asked Liu Lai-tzu. I did not answer because I was thinking of something else, but went along with him.

After unloading the rice, I went back to the guest room where, despite my abhorrence of the whole pack of them,

I had to pour them wine. Every time I sent in a dish, I'd look at Hu Han-san, at his villainous features, his short moustache and cunning, shifty eyes. Was there no end to these people's eating, drinking and raucous laughter!

"I'm thinking of acquiring a few dozen *mu* of land in the country for my daughter," said Shen to Hu Han-san. "I hope you will help me."

"I'll look into it," replied Hu. "If I can, I'll certainly be glad to."

"Commander Hu," put in the police chief, "if you have any rice to sell, just get in touch with proprietor Shen direct. He'll give you a good price."

"I'm afraid I'll be troubling him a lot now that we know each other." And so, on and on.

I came to understand even better that the local despots who oppressed the poor peasants, the town proprietors who hoarded and speculated, the police chiefs, the White guards, and the Japanese militarists, were all of a gang. They all lorded it over our villages and towns. As I was thinking this, I almost spilled a large tureen of soup over Hu Han-san's long gown. Shen gave me a biting look while Hu Han-san said with a forced grin, "It doesn't matter." Then, turning round, he asked me, "What's your surname?" I did not want to betray myself by letting him hear my local dialect, so I took the tray and left the room. Only when I reached the threshold did I murmur, "My family name is Kuo."

If Hu Han-san spotted me — just the boy he was looking for — he would kill me. I must not fall into his hands, or I wouldn't be able to avenge myself. What could I do? I couldn't go and ask Uncle Chao for he'd left his old place. I must make a plan. I did not return to the guest room, but went to find Liu Lai-tzu and asked him to finish waiting on the guests. I tied my clothes into a bundle and went up front to the shop where I sat down behind the counter to think. I must not let this villain of a local despot, my mortal enemy, get away this time.

"Winter Boy!" came Shen's voice from the guest room after the feast was over. "Come and help the guest to the west room to rest." I went. Hu Han-san's face was ghastly with drink, the veins in his eyes distended with blood.

"What's your name?" he bawled, one hand clutching at my shoulder.

"Kuo Chen-shan."

"Kuo, did you say?"

"Yes, Kuo," I answered calmly.

"Where do you come from?" Hu Han-san was no longer smiling. His drunken red eyes shone cold and malignant.

"From Kuo River just outside the city."

"You're not a native of this county!" Hu Han-san's hand clawed into my shoulder so that I could feel his nails cutting into my flesh.

"He's drunk," I said to Shen, and tried to break loose from Hu's grasp to get away.

"Don't go. So I'm drunk. You must help me into the room," said Hu Han-san, grinning. And he insisted

77

that I should see him to his room even though Shen offered to do it himself.

"Lie down," I said, suppressing my anger and hatred. "I'll fetch some water for you to wash your face."

Once out of the room I could think of nothing but vengeance. But how? I thought hard. In the kitchen, where I got the hot water, I saw a hatchet lying beside a pile of kindling. "A weapon!" I thought to myself. Better hide it. And I put it behind the kitchen door. Then I went back to the west room with the hot water.

Hu Han-san had already taken off his long gown, and his pistol lay beside his pillow. I put the basin of hot water on the wash stand and started to leave the room. "Stop!" Hu's voice bellowed behind me, and I did, without turning around.

"Is your mother at home?" he asked.

The words stabbed like a dagger. If the hatchet had been in my hand at that moment, I'm sure I'd have hacked him to death. But I held back my anger and replied, "No, she's not."

"Is she dead?"

"No, she's alive."

"Where is she?"

"With my uncle at South Mountain."

"Huh!" Hu Han-san took a step towards me. "Turn round and face me!"

"What for?" I demanded, turning suddenly to look him boldly in the eye.

"And your father?" pursued Hu Han-san, fingering his pistol, now in his hand.

78

"He's at home."

"What does he do?"

"He's a butcher. He kills pigs."

Hu took another step nearer. "Does he kill people?" I looked at him defiantly, ignoring his question.

"You're lying." And he pointed his pistol at me. "You're the son of Pan Hsing-yi of Willow Brook Village!"

"No, I'm not," said I shaking my head. "My father is Kuo Shan-jen."

"Huh!" went on Hu Han-san, showing his teeth in a treacherous grin. "You shall not leave this room tonight. Tomorrow you go back to Willow Brook with me. Do you hear?"

The enemy had recognized me. What was I to do? I'd rush at him, grab his pistol, and shoot! But just then Liu Lai-tzu came into the room. "Your mother's come to see you, Kuo Chen-shan," said he. "She's waiting outside." While Hu Han-san was trying to figure that one out I seized the chance to leave the room.

Liu Lai-tzu led me to the shop counter where I took his hand as an expression of the gratitude I felt. In the past year and a half I had confided to him about my family — my father, mother and myself. He not only sympathized with me but tried to help me in every way. Now, hearing Hu Han-san cross-examining me, he made up the story about my mother coming to see me.

Liu Lai-tzu looked around and, seeing no one about, asked, "Who's that man? Why should he point his gun at you?"

"He's the murderer of my mother!" I told him.

"So that's why he stared at you like that during the feast! And I heard him say he was going to take you back to Willow Brook. I guessed it might be him. . . ."

"How can I ever thank you!"

"You got away this time. But what about tomorrow? If Hu Han-san wants to take you away the boss won't stop him." I didn't answer for fear he might stop me if I told him what I planned to do.

Night fell. The oldest apprentice had gone home on leave and Liu Lai-tzu and I were lying on our pallets. Liu Lai-tzu advised me to run away under cover of darkness and I said I would, but asked him to go to sleep first.

As for me, I could think of no way but to kill this class enemy — or I'd be killed by him.

I stole out of bed and put my little bundle on the counter, then made my way towards the kitchen. It was pitch dark, for the moon hadn't risen yet. I found the kitchen door locked and tried the window. It was not latched. So I pushed it open to get into the kitchen. My hand landed on a box of matches, and I thought immediately of fire. I seemed to see my mother looking at me. Ah, fire! Hu Han-san, you burned my mother to death, and by fire you shall die! Yes, that's it. He was drunk and must be sleeping like a pig. If his room burned down, he wouldn't have much chance of getting out.

I put the box of matches into my pocket, then lugged in an armful of dry rushes. I tiptoed to the west room. The lights were out and I pushed the door open. Hu Han-san lay snoring. I put the dry rushes under his bed and struck a match. They were instantly alight and I hurried out of the room, tying the door shut with a piece of rope. You'll soon be ashes, you scoundrel!" I said to myself as I made for the shop counter.

I felt satisfied with what I had done. Then I looked at Liu Lai-tzu lying there fast asleep and said, "I'm leaving you now, Lai-tzu."

I took up my little bundle and silently opened the door. I looked back once at the back compound. Smoke was coming from the window of the west room, followed by

tongues of flame. I felt my heart as warm as the fire. Then I heard someone shouting in the room and trying to open the door from the inside. The boss's wife shouted from the east room: "Fire! The west room's on fire!" This was followed by the voice of the boss himself, yelling, "Hurry, hurry! Put out the fire!" The couple rushed from their room to wake up their guest. They called, but there was no answer. They tried the door but it was still tied shut. So they had to undo the knot before dashing in and dragging the man out. Only after some time did he come to and mutter, "Grab that boy. . . . Arrest . . . him. . . ." By this time the boss's wife began to beat on a brass basin as a fire alarm.

I couldn't stay in that place any longer, so I left by the shop door and ran. . . .

It was not until I came to a highway outside the county town that I began to slow down and take my breath. I was fairly safe, for they wouldn't be able to overtake me. I walked and walked, thinking of many things. Where could I go? Home to Willow Brook? Out of the question. And Uncle Sung was in prison. How about the guerrillas? Where were they now? Suddenly I thought of Yenan! Hadn't Brother Wu told me that my father had gone to Yenan with Chairman Mao? Yes, Yenan was where I'd go. But where was Yenan? How quiet it was! A new moon was rising, and I located the North Star. I'd follow that, for I remembered Brother Wu saying that Yenan was in the north. Filling my lungs with the night air, I started walking, guided by that star. . . .

VII

Like a bird out of a cage, I flew towards the north, on and on without stopping, the new moon dimly lighting my way and the North Star my compass. It was so quiet that my own footsteps sounded loud in my ears. Climbing hills and crossing streams, I kept my direction. Tired after climbing, I sat down on the bank of a rivulet to rest in the gentle spring breeze and scooped up a couple of handfuls of water to drink. How soft the sound of the water! How bracing the air! I took a deep breath, and was refreshed and happy. A heavy load was gone from my chest. No longer were my ears assailed by the shrill voice of that skeleton woman. No more the disgusting sight of her daughter sucking lollipops. No more waiting on the fat-headed proprietor, or standing behind the counter selling poor people rice mixed with gravel. . . . My year and a half of drudgery in that rice shop was over. There was the crowing of roosters from afar. It would soon be light, and I must hurry. I picked up my little bundle and was on my way again.

How rosy and beautiful the dawn was that morning! At the rice shop I would be taking down the shutters, sweeping out the place, waiting on the boss and his family. I never had the chance to enjoy the beauty of a sunrise. But today, as I stopped under a small tree, I looked for a long time at the morning sky in the east. Fields of paddy reflected the pink of the clouds, the rice seedlings jewelled with morning dew. A bird flew down from its nest in a tree chirping and then soared into the sky. Everything was so fresh and bright. I felt all the more that it was right for me to leave that suffocating rice shop.

Arriving at a village, I suddenly felt hungry and went to a small food stand under straw matting to get a bowl of rice. The old woman who ran the stand asked me where I came from and where I was headed for. I said I came from the mountains and was visiting relatives.

"You must have been walking the whole night," she said.

I was startled. "How do you know?" I asked.

"Your clothes and shoes are all covered with dew and mud!"

This immediately put me on the alert. If Hu Han-san's men were after me, I thought, they too would recognize these signs and I'd better not linger. So I gulped down the rice and left. No one was on the road, and I went back to ask where the nearest town was.

"It depends on which town you're going to," replied the woman. "There's one forty *li* south of here, and another fifty *li* north. Which way are you going?"

"North." I left the mat shed and started walking north.

Obviously I'd gone only forty *li*, for the town to the south would be the one I'd just left and Hu Han-san's

84

men could soon overtake me. The road would not be safe. I must hide out for some time. I left the road and made for a hill in the distance.

I found the hill steeper and higher than it had appeared, and I half crawled up, reaching the top quite out of breath. Feeling safe there I sat down on a rock to rest. The place was beautiful, with green trees and bamboo. The sun had risen, warming and cheering me. I had never felt so carefree in the past year and a half. I stretched out with my little bundle under my head and went to sleep.

I was awakened by the sound of voices. Peering from my wooded sanctuary, I saw two "peace preservation" men in olive-green jackets escorting an old woman, whom I recognized as the keeper of the food stand where I had stopped to eat. I heard the two men ask her, "Didn't a boy climb up that mountain?"

"I didn't see any boy!" she answered.

"Someone saw the boy climbing that mountain," said one of the men.

"I didn't see anyone climb the mountain."

"Ah, let's go back," said the other. "Why bother? We're just wearing out our shoes and nobody's going to give us new ones, that's sure."

"But if we catch that boy, we'll get the fifty-silver-dollar reward."

"Why do you want to get that boy?" asked the old woman.

"He's the son of a Communist. He made a fire, tried to kill somebody."

85

The old woman looked up the mountain. "I don't think he could be hiding there. There are no Communists on that mountain." The two men ignored her and started climbing. I immediately moved on to another hilltop.

There, I climbed a tree with thick leaves, and hid myself. It wasn't long till the two "peace preservation" men arrived, looked around for a while and then, swearing at their ill luck, went back down the hill.

How was it possible, I asked myself, for Hu Han-san to order the "peace preservation corps" of this county to search for me? It became clear that these scoundrels were all linked up; they were all against the Communists. Their bosses gave the order, and they would carry it out, especially if there was a fifty-silver-dollar reward!

The sun was setting and I left my tree perch, but dared not go down the hill lest the men in yellow jackets still lurked there. But I was so hungry it was painful. And I could not find any wild fruit around. Then I remembered what my father told me when he was having the bullet taken out. "If you refuse to feel the pain, the pain will stop." Now, I was very hungry, but I'd try not to feel it. I thought then of my father and the Red Army, tried to guess when they'd be back. The White guards were exploiting and bullying the people, the landlords had seized back the land, and the poor people couldn't get rice to eat. And now here were Hu Han-san's men searching for me. How they hated the Red Army and their offspring! The people here all looked forward to the day when the Red Army would be back again. Suddenly I was aware of a flock of wild geese overhead, flying in V-formation. If only one would come down and take my message to Yenan!

After sundown, when a mist had risen, I hurried down the hill and, making sure I was on the road north, strode on vigorously.

Tired and hungry as I was, I kept on, fired by the thought of reaching Yenan, seeing my father, making revolution with Chairman Mao, and bringing back the Red

Army to avenge my mother! My legs ached, my feet were blistered, but by dawn I had reached the outskirts of another county town.

There was an eating place but, though I was famished, the money I had would buy only a bowl of gruel and some griddle cakes and fritters. I would have to beg from now on. I must get to Yenan even if I had to beg all the way!

I walked another day, begging. Then, the next morning it started to rain, and I found the going very difficult. I came to a village, went into a cowshed and sat down. How cold it was! I opened my bundle and put on the jacket mother gave me, then I thought of her, and the night before my father went away to join the Red Army. He had said to mother, "If our Worker-Peasant Democratic Government remains here, send him to the Lenin primary school." There'd been no chance to go to the Lenin primary school, but life in these years had taught me many things. Who had forced me to wander in these mountains? It was Hu Han-san, proprietor Shen, the police chief and the White guards. They all belonged to the class that oppressed me. How I yearned to find Dad! To make revolution together with him, with Chairman Mao to lead, so as to overthrow the class that oppressed us. I felt the hem of my jacket for the red star which father gave me and which mother sewed into my clothes. At once I found strength to continue my trek.

The rain had slackened, and I walked into the village to see if I could get something to eat. Two families, appearing not well off, gave me some left-over rice. Then

I passed a house with a high gate. A black dog rushed out barking, and before I could get away the beast took a bite out of my leg, which began to bleed. I picked up a stone and aimed it at the dog's head so that it yelped and ran away. A man came out of the house. He was middle-aged, fat and sallow-looking, with no eyebrows but rat-like eyes, a flat nose, big mouth and thin moustache. He wore a satin skull cap. I didn't need to look twice to know that this was not a good man. "Are you a beggar?" he demanded. When I didn't answer he asked again, "What are you begging for?"

"I'm hungry from walking and brought nothing with me," I replied. When he asked me where I came from, I became suspicious and answered only vaguely, "The mountains."

"And your home folks?" he continued.

"I've got none."

"Only yourself?"

"Only myself."

"Where are you going?"

"Nowhere."

"Well, I'll find you a place where you can have something to eat." Then he added, "Right here."

"What's the work?" I asked, on guard now.

"Cowherd for me, and you can do odd jobs as well. I'll feed you."

Now I was certain. He was a landlord, trying to make me his farmhand. "No!" I said emphatically, turned on my heel and went away. The man yelled after me: "Beggar! If I catch you again in my village I'll break your legs!"

I wouldn't be cowed; I headed straight for the village. The man picked up a stick and hit me with it. "Get out!" he yelled. "I won't have you in my village." Mad with rage, I picked up a handful of mud and flung it in his face, right in his eyes! I grabbed the stick and gave him two good whacks, then ran out of the village.

On the top of a hill not far from the village was a small temple. I climbed up to it and found it quite deserted, the gate open. In the courtyard was a tall ging-ko tree. The rooms on the east and west were locked, but the one on the north was wide open and I went in. The place was thick with dust. An idol with a gilded face stood on its pedestal, but there were no incense-burners or candle-sticks in front of it, as though no wor-shippers had been there for a long time. I brushed the dust off a long stone bench and spread my thin cotton mattress on it, took off my wet clothes and lay down. Dead tired, I was soon fast asleep.

I woke up in the middle of the night. All round was pitch dark. The wind was howling as though it would uproot the gingko tree and even blow the small temple away. My clothes were not yet dry and I was very cold and very hungry. I groped inside my bundle and put on all the clothes I had, then wrapped myself in my thin cotton coverlet. I tried to go to sleep again but couldn't. Awake, I felt the cold and hunger more un-bearable and the night, so dark, endless.

At last the wind died down, but dawn was slow in coming. Then, at the first glimmer of light outside, I jumped down from the high stone bench and went out of the temple.

The sun was up and shone on the temple wall, illuminating slogans that had all but been washed away by the seasons of rain: "Smash the local tyrants! Divide up their land!" The words gave me strength. So the people here had also made revolution. And, though they now groaned under White rule, the Red Army would return some day, the local tyrants would again be overthrown, land again divided, and the revolution would succeed.

I went back to the temple to tie up my bundle, then went down the hill and headed for the village, hoping to find something to eat to sustain me on my journey.

People were at their meal when I reached the village, and I was given two bowls of gruel by a family which appeared not at all well-to-do. It was such people, I found, who sympathized with the poor. I was about to leave the village when I met a schoolboy of perhaps thirteen or fourteen dressed in fine clothes, a satchel over his shoulder, his hair well groomed. He was munching a sweet rice cake. He brushed near me, stopped and said challengingly, "Hey, little begger, call me papa and I'll give you a piece of this rice cake." The insult was more than I could take, but in order to avoid a row I said nothing and went on my way. The brat turned to face me, then throwing the piece of cake on the ground, said, "Eat it, doggy, eat it!" I could stand no more! I kicked that piece of cake and it landed about ten feet away! At that, he bawled, "Pay me back, pay me back my rice cake!"

"Yes, I'll pay you back," I said angrily. Smack! Smack! I gave him two slaps in the face, leaving red finger prints.

"Come, somebody, quick! This beggar slapped me." The boy clung to me and roared like a wild animal. I threw him to the ground, but the cunning brat got hold of my leg and I couldn't get free no matter how hard I kicked.

The rumpus brought people out of their houses to see what was going on. Among them was an old woman who came over and whispered to me sympathetically, "Look! See what you've done. Got yourself into trouble. Hurry and run away! If the boy's father comes out, it'll be the end of you."

Another, a middle-aged man, said, "That's the son of Wu, the head of the tithing office. He can do what he likes to you. Why did you slap him?" And he tried to loosen the boy's hold on my leg so I could run away. But a man was approaching, yelling and scolding. I looked up, and there I saw — the very man I'd thrown mud at! When the boy saw the man, he bawled, "Daddy, come quick!"

The man grabbed my shoulder and dragged me along. I knew it would be useless to reason with him, so I kept my mouth shut. A crowd had gathered, and the woman who had befriended me tried to put in a good word for me. But the man looked at her fiercely and yelled, "I won't let him go this time. I'll skin him alive!" Two of the landlord's men came along, tied my hands behind my back, and took me to the courtyard of that house with a high gate. They strung me up on a locust tree and beat me with a carrying pole. The brat added in a few hard lashes with a whip. I felt the pain at first, but gradually I was numbed, until I lost consciousness completely.

When I finally came to, I tried to turn over but couldn't move. All my bones felt like they were broken. I opened my eyes with great effort. Where was I? I was lying on a river bank. An old man of over fifty was sitting beside me.

"You're. . . ." But my tongue was thick and refused to move.

"I just passed by. My name's Yao. I saw Wu of the tithing office beat you up and throw you here. I was

93

afraid wild animals might get you. I've been sitting here for a long time watching you."

"Thank you. . . ." Then I suddenly remembered my little bundle.

"What are you looking for?" asked my benefactor.

"My bundle."

"Wu took it away."

Now all I had left were the few clothes on my back. My mother's jacket, which I had on had been torn to shreds by those rowdies. But I was happy when I felt the red star still there in the hem! It made me think again of Yenan, my destination.

I tried to get up but couldn't, even with the kind old man's help. "You'd better lie still. You're all bruises."

"But I must go."

"Where to?"

By this time I was convinced he was a good man. So I said, "Yenan."

The old man looked around before asking, "What for?"

"To look for Dad."

"Ah, but it's very, very far away," he said with a soft sigh.

"I have to go there, no matter how far it is."

"How can you walk? Look at your legs!" he reminded me.

I lifted one leg. It might have been made of wood and the other was no better, the joints so stiff that they wouldn't bend at all. But I must get to Yenan, to my father and the Red Army, and I tried crawling.

You'd better go home with me for a while," said the old man sympathetically.

"Where do you live?" I asked.

"In Yao Pond Village, about ten *li* away."

The distance sounded formidable, but then the old man said, "I'll carry you there on my back."

I was so moved that tears came to my eyes. "'How can I ever thank you," I said over and over.

"I have someone in Yenan too, my boy," he said seriously. "My son, Hai-chuan, went with Chairman Mao on the Long March. We're like gourds from the same vine."

VIII

It was already dark when we reached the old man's home. He put me up in his room. "Hurry up and come here, Hsiao-hung's Ma" he called out, and soon a woman came into the room. "Who is this boy?" she asked, looking surprised.

"My family name is Pan — Pan Chen-shan," I introduced myself. She asked me where I came from.

"I picked him up on the river bank," the old man explained, adding, "That tithing office head Wu nearly beat him to death. Quick! Get water to wash his wounds."

A girl about twelve came into the room in answer to the woman's call. "Hsiao-hung, hurry and put some water on to boil," said the woman.

The old man told us three his plan. "From now on, Chen-shan will stay with us. If anyone asks," he said

95

looking at his wife, "just say he's your nephew." He looked at me and said, "Call her Aunt and me Uncle." Then, indicating the girl, he continued, "She's my daughter Hsiao-hung. You two will be cousins."

The girl, watching the kettle on the stove, gave me a smile, and I felt very grateful for all these arrangements. But I wouldn't stay here long, for I had to go to Yenan. "Thank you, Uncle," I said, "but I have to go as soon as I'm well enough."

"You can't just go like that — into the void," said Uncle Yao. "You have to contact the Party organizations." On our way I had told Uncle Yao my story from the time I left Uncle Sung's place till I was taken to that rice shop to be an apprentice. "The thing for you to do now," he continued, "is to find Uncle Chao, or Secretary Wu."

"But how can I find them?" I said.

"Stay here for the time being. I'll help you find them."

"Yes, you just stay here, and consider this as your own home," Aunt Yao joined in. So I had found a home again! I stayed on.

How different life was in Uncle Yao's home from that in the rice shop! There I was always weighed down by something; here I found warmth and home life. Uncle and Aunt Yao, cousin Hsiao-hung and myself had the same hopes and shared the same feelings. I felt like a member of their family.

The wound on my right leg got infected and hadn't healed after two and a half months' treatment. I got worried. How was I to make the 25,000-*li* journey to Yenan? One rainy day when the four of us were at home chatting, I pointed to the wound on my leg and said, "In Willow Brook I was beaten by Hu Han-san; in the rice shop proprietor Shen beat me, at Forked River that fellow Wu did this. What right had they to beat me. . . ?"

"They have money, and power," said Aunt Yao.

"They have guns in their hands, their 'peace preservation corps,' police bureau . . ." added Uncle Yao.

"They're of the same breed as the reactionary government officials," sighed Aunt.

"If our Worker-Peasant Democratic Government were still here, and the Red Army hadn't gone, such rascals would be tied up and paraded in tall paper hats like Hu Han-san," I said. "But as it is, they stomp over us like despots."

"The Red Army will come back, and the day will come when the poor will be liberated," said Uncle Yao confidently. Uncle Yao knew a lot about the revolution, and he told us many stories about it.

In the autumn of that year we heard from people who had come from the city that the Japanese had surrendered and that we had won the victory in our war against Japan. We all felt very happy. I said, laughing, to Uncle Yao, "Dad and Brother Hai-chuan will soon come back, and the Red Army, too."

"We'll have to wait and see," Uncle Yao said calmly.

But why? I thought to myself. Hadn't the Red Army gone north to fight the Japanese? Now that they had surrendered, the Red Army should come back.

Soon after, Uncle Yao went to the county seat again to look for Uncle Chao, but again failed to find him. What he heard was that the Kuomintang reactionaries were hurrying up from the rear to accept the Japanese surrender, but that the Eighth Route Army, which bore the brunt of the fighting in the anti-Japanese War, forbade the Kuomintang to seize the fruits of victory, as the Kuomintang had actually sabotaged the resistance war. He heard there that fighting might break out.

The situation developed as the people said, and became tense. The "central government army" and the Kuomintang ruling clique robbed the people and grabbed whatever they could lay their hands on. Since the Kuomintang army had come, exacting grain, food, taxes and almost anything you could think of, life had become extremely difficult for the people.

One day when Hsiao-hung and I were returning from gathering firewood, we saw two armed Kuomintang soldiers near the door of our house, with a tithing chief standing guard. Inside was another soldier carrying a pistol. I heard Uncle say, "Only yesterday you were here and took away what little money I had, and today you come again!"

"What we took yesterday was 'welcome' money," said the soldier. "Today we want 'comfort' money!"

"Yes, yes," put in the tithing chief, "the Kuomintang Army fought hard and won merit. They deserve bonuses."

"What merit?" Uncle glared at the tithing chief, who had no answer and could only look appealingly at the soldier. "Don't waste time," bawled the soldier. "Hand over your money."

"I have no money. It's all been taken away."

"No money?" bawled the soldier again. "Give us rice instead, then."

"I have no rice either, not even to feed my family."

"You old rogue. You refuse to contribute. . . ?" threatened the soldier, pointing his pistol at Uncle. At this moment the tithing chief went out and whispered something to one of the soldiers there. The soldier came into the house and reported in a loud voice, "Platoon leader, this old man's son is a Communist!"

"Ah, so that's it," said the platoon leader, glowering at Uncle. "No wonder you dare to resist my demand. So your son's an Eighth Route Army man. You'd better know where you are. If you don't hand over your money I'll have you arrested."

"Do whatever you like, I have no money, neither have I rice," Uncle said calmly.

That devil of a platoon leader gave Uncle a slap in the face, and, turning, shouted at the two soldiers, "Search the place!" Then everything in the house was turned upside down.

"What kind of army are you, robbing the people?" Uncle said vehemently, pushing the soldiers aside. One of them hit Uncle with the butt of his rifle and Uncle fell to the floor.

When I saw that I was furious and picked up the knife I chopped firewood with. I was rushing into the house with it when Hsiao-hung, fearing I might make things worse, dragged me back. Meanwhile, Uncle had seen me and said, "Let them rob!"

99

A soldier discovered a basket half full of rice and yelped with joy. As expected, he took it away, basket and all!

How could we stand it! Even little Hsiao-hung was angry. "These beasts!" said Uncle, setting his teeth. "Until they're wiped out we'll have a hard time just to live!"

True enough, life was even harder after the Kuomintang soldiers came. They said we were relatives of the Reds, and hated us. They thought of every way to persecute us.

Uncle tried secretly to glean news about the Communist Party and the Red Army. We knew that the Red Army had been renamed the Eighth Route Army and the New Fourth Army, and was now the People's Liberation Army. Also that this army of several tens of thousands of men now had more than a million men over the entire country. It was fighting the Kuomintang forces in the north. We were very happy to hear that the Red Army had grown in numbers and had more arms, and that the base areas had grown in size. All this was good news, but we were too far away. I wanted to start my journey northward again to find the Liberation Army, but Uncle wouldn't hear of it. He said we had to find the Party organization before I could go.

We tried and tried, waited and waited, till another year was gone.

One day Uncle was called to the tithing office. After a long time he came back, looking very grave. When Aunt asked him what was the matter he didn't answer, just kept puffing at his pipe. "What's the matter, Uncle?" I ventured.

"They want to pressgang you into the Kuomintang army!" Uncle finally blurted out.

"We mustn't let him go!" Aunt said emphatically.

"If he doesn't go, we've got to give two piculs of rice instead. That's what they said at the tithing office."

"Two piculs?" I was shocked. Where were we to get two piculs of rice!

"They know very well that we don't have two piculs of rice. It's only meant to make things awkward for us," Uncle explained.

"What are we going to do then?" Aunt was worried.

"I'll go north to find the Liberation Army," said I.

"And I'll go to the hills tomorrow to gather medicinal herbs for money on your way," Uncle declared.

I was so moved that I just looked at Uncle, unable to say a word.

That night we prepared the implements we would need. Hsiao-hung and I were to go along with Uncle.

The next morning after breakfast as we were about to start, Uncle said, "You two had better take along the choppers and two carrying poles."

"Are we going to gather so many herbs, Uncle?" I asked.

"How can there be so many herbs?" said Uncle. "These things are for gathering firewood." I still didn't know what he meant, so he explained. "This is for camouflage. If we carry two loads of firewood, no one will suspect us. We must avoid the attention of the Kuomintang army." Uncle was certainly very vigilant.

As I was leaving to search for my father and the Liberation Army, I thought of my mother's jacket and the red star sewed into the hem. I would take these with me. So I asked Aunt to take out the jacket and I wrapped it together with my other things into a little bundle. Aunt handed me four hard-boiled eggs from the pot and said, "Here, take these along." I looked at her and reluctantly bade her goodbye.

She took both my hands into hers as she said, "Look for Hai-chuan, too, if you can."

"I will," said I. "And when I've found him, I'll come back with him."

Aunt saw us off at the door. I looked back after we had gone some distance and saw that she was still standing at the door.

We came to a mountain pass where towering before us were high peaks half enveloped in cloud and mist. The mountain paths were rugged and often cut by hills and valleys. About mid-day we stopped at the foot of a precipice. I looked up and saw clusters of bamboo and vines covering it. Two eagles were circling high above. The peak was so steep that it seemed in some places almost to project outward. Uncle got ready to climb it by tying the basket to his shoulder and fastening round his waist a belt to which a metal hook was attached. He then took off his shoes and started climbing.

Uncle gathered medicinal herbs up there while Hsiao-hung and I cut firewood below. I would look up at Uncle suspended half way of the precipice gathering medicinal plants for me and feel grateful to the bottom of my heart!

Because I was the son of a Red Army man he saved my life and took me into his family though he'd never seen me before. And now, to save me from being pressganged into the Kuomintang army, this old Uncle was risking his life to get money for my journey to find our own people's army. "What is this but class feeling?" I said to myself.

Hsiao-hung noticed I'd stopped chopping brushwood and asked me what I was thinking about. "Are you coming back after you've found the guerrillas?" she asked.

"No," I replied. "That is," I hastened to add, "not until we've wiped out the Kuomintang reactionaries and their White guards."

"What if that takes a long time?"

"I'll fight them my whole life then."

Hsiao-hung looked at me and smiled.

"Do you sometimes think of your brother Hai-chuan?" I asked.

"Yes, of course. But I can't remember what he looks like. He went away when I was only three," she replied.

"You know, I want to be like your brother — join the Liberation Army and fight through the years to wipe out the White guards and build socialism."

"Then you two can come back together."

An eagle circled overhead, and Hsiao-hung looked up to watch it. "How I wish I could go with you!" said she. "You and my brother are like that eagle, flying so high, so far!" We watched the eagle spread its wings wide and fly higher and higher till it disappeared.

Hsiao-hung and I had gathered four bundles of firewood, and Uncle had come down with the herbs. We rested for a while. Then Uncle said to Hsiao-hung, "You go home first. Tell mother I'm going to walk a way with Chen-shan." Hsiao-hung nodded. "And if anyone asks, no matter who," Uncle added, "just say that we've gone to visit relatives." Hsiao-hung nodded again. "And if the tithing office chief comes for rice," he continued, "tell him that I've gone to borrow some." And once again Hsiao-hung nodded. She never said a word, but stood on a rock and watched us go down the hill, each carrying two bundles of firewood on a pole.

We came to a county seat and went into a big medicine shop to sell the herbs, leaving the baskets of firewood outside the shop. When the clerk saw the herbs which Uncle had laid on the counter, he exclaimed in surprise and delight, "So we've finally got this medicine!" Then he turned round and called out, "Mr. Han, someone's brought in the medicine regiment commander Hu's so anxious to get."

From behind the counter appeared a tall, lean man wearing spectacles who glanced at the medicine and said hurriedly, "Take it! Take it!" Then, to Uncle, he added, "Bring in more of this," and paid us for the herbs.

When Uncle and I came out of the shop, there were three Kuomintang soldiers in olive-green uniform standing by our bundles of firewood. "Whose are these?" they asked, pointing at the bundles.

"Mine," replied Uncle.

"Sell them to us," one of the soldiers said.

These four bundles of firewood were used as a camouflage and were not for sale, but since these soldiers wanted them Uncle set a high price. "Five yuan for the two bundles," said Uncle.

"All right. Come with us. You'll get your money when we reach there."

What could Uncle and I do but carry the firewood and follow those soldiers? We walked quite some distance and then came to a big courtyard where many Kuomintang soldiers were billeted. We were told to take the firewood to the kitchen. When Uncle asked the soldier where the money was, he said, "We have no money today. Come again after half a month."

"But we need the money. We only sell for cash."

"Damn you!" cursed the soldier. "What difference does half a month make? You'd have to give it to us even if we didn't pay at all!"

Argument was useless, so I picked up the load and started off. One of the soldiers grabbed me and kicked me in the leg, saying, "Where do you think you're going? Put that wood down."

I was so mad, I threw the load down and said angrily, "What do you think you're doing? Buying things without paying for them. Hitting people instead!"

A quarrel ensued which attracted the attention of a Kuomintang army officer, who appeared on the scene from a high-walled house. He walked over and asked, "What's going on here?"

"He wants our two loads of firewood," Uncle managed to say, pointing at the soldier, "but says he has no money to pay for them today. We need the money."

"Ah . . ." the officer commented. "How much can two loads of firewood cost? Why all the fuss? We wouldn't cheat you."

One of the soldiers walked over to the officer and whispered, "We haven't been paid for two months. We haven't got any money. . . ."

The officer lowered his gaze, turned and started back towards the house.

I knew the officer was only making a gesture. The higher their rank, the more they exploited the people. And how could we expect the soldiers to pay for the firewood? The transaction was pure robbery from top to bottom.

Just then, the tall thin man in spectacles that I'd seen at the medicine shop came over, a red paper box in his hand. He went straight to the officer and said, "Regiment Commander Hu, I've got the medicine you want. Fresh from the mountains this morning."

"So you've got it. Good!" The officer was all smiles. "You must have gone to a lot of trouble."

"No more than we ought to," said the man in spectacles, bowing low. "But these rare herbs are really very difficult to get, fresh ones especially. We sent a person up the mountain just to get them."

"Is the medicine really good for the after-effects of burns?" queried the officer, taking the red box in his hands.

"Oh yes!" The man in spectacles straightened up and said flamboyantly, "This medicine, Commander Hu, relaxes the tendons, stimulates circulation, promotes tissue growth and restores youth!" With that he took out a piece of paper and said, "Here are the directions for taking the medicine."

"We really owe you a great deal," replied the officer. Then, turning towards the house, he called, "Adjutant Ma!"

Shouting "Here!" a man rushed out of the house — evidently Adjutant Ma.

"Rush this medicine to Willow Brook. Tell my father that Mr. Han of the Tai Ho Tang medicine shop specially got it for him. It's for the after-effects of burns. Go by bicycle."

"No need to send it," replied the adjutant. "We've just received a letter from your father. He says he's coming over this afternoon."

Regiment Commander Hu! With a father at Willow Brook! Medicine for the after-effects of burns! Coming this afternoon! The sun was already in the western sky, my mortal enemy would be coming any time now! Uncle and I exchanged looks and immediately left that place.

We had gone only a few steps out of the courtyard when I heard the bell of a ricksha. Looking up, I saw sitting in it a middle-aged man in a grey gown and black felt hat. His face bore the scars of burns, but his eyes still had the same wolfish look. The local despot Hu Han-san had unfortunately survived the fire! The sight of him again made my blood boil. When Hu's gaze fell in my direction, Uncle walked over in front of me, and when Hu was alighting from the ricksha, we turned the corner onto another street.

We walked steadily and were soon out of the county seat.

IX

Uncle and I walked another twenty *li*. It was getting dark, and we found a night's lodging in a little village. The next day, when Uncle wanted to accompany me further, I pleaded with him saying, "Please don't, Uncle. You're too old to stand such a hard journey." He wanted to go a short distance more but I wouldn't hear of it. "These years of hardship have trained me. I know how to handle those ruffians now," I insisted.

Uncle drew from his pocket the money he had got for the herbs and said, "Take this with you." When I took only two of the banknotes, he pressed the whole lot into my hands, saying, "Take them all!"

With a deep feeling of gratitude for everything Uncle Yao had done for me all these years, I accepted the money reluctantly, and went on my way, alone again.

Towards evening the next day I came to a small market town and went into an inn. There were no lodgers; only the innkeeper was there, a man who looked to be over fifty. I took my bundle off my back and lay down to rest. As I was very tired, I was soon asleep.

During the night I was awakened by loud knocks at the door. "Open up! Open up!" came surly voices from outside. There were the same loud knocks at neighbouring doors. I was out of bed in a flash, grabbed my little bundle and escaped by the window. Once out in the darkness, I saw through the window the innkeeper going to the door and asking, "Who's there? What do you want?"

"Hurry and open up!" I heard someone shouting and kicking at the door.

The innkeeper opened the door, and in rushed a crowd of men, one flashing a torch in the darkness. It was a bunch of Kuomintang soldiers! I climbed onto a low wall nearby and from there jumped onto the roof so I could see what was going on.

"What do you want?" the innkeeper asked nervously.

"Get us a couple of men to carry our things for us."

"Every two or three days you come for porters. Nobody dares to lodge here." The flashlight beam landed on the innkeeper. "You mean me? But I'm nearly sixty, old and sick. I can hardly carry anything." The beam suddenly shifted to the bunk where I had just been sleeping. "Where's the occupant of that bed?"

"Gone. He ran away."

"So he's run away, but you're still here. Come with us, sick or not." And two soldiers with guns stepped forward to drag the innkeeper away. He argued with them but to no avail. They beat him up and took him away.

I lay flat on the roof, listening to cries of women and children from adjacent houses. How angry I was! The night was dark, but not so dark as that old society. It must be smashed!

When the noise died away, I crept down from the roof and left the inn, again trekking northward in big strides.

Rain or shine, by day and under starry skies, I walked, always northward. I could think of only one thing and that was to find the Party organization and the Liberation Army as soon as possible. Then I could join the revolutionary ranks and, under the leadership of Chairman Mao, fight together with the Liberation Army to overthrow the dark old society with its gangs of wolves like Hu Han-san.

On and on I walked, inquiring from time to time about the situation. People said that the Liberation Army was fighting the Kuomintang army north of the Yangtze River and that many places had been liberated. I was greatly heartened and headed for the Yangtze River, finally reaching it one afternoon.

What a mighty river it was, roaring and billowing! I had seen rivers before, and I had swum in them, too, but not rivers like this one. Standing there on the bank, I could see nothing but a vast expanse of water and some small boats bobbing up and down with the waves. The opposite bank was hidden in the distant mists.

I walked along the riverside, hoping to come to a ferry. People said the Goat's Horn Ferry was some three *li* away. When I got there, I noticed a knot of people gathered round, and at the gate to the ferry two Kuomintang soldiers shouting to those who wanted to cross the river, "Show your pass! Show your pass!"

How was I to produce any "pass"! There was little chance of crossing here, so I turned away, not to ask for trouble. As I walked, I looked at the Yangtze and thought

to myself, no matter how wide and deep you are, or how high your waves, I'll get to the other side, somehow!

But to swim across the Yangtze might attract attention and arouse suspicion. So I sat on the bank waiting for it to get dark. The sun was setting now, casting a pink glow on the surface of the water. Many thoughts rose in my mind, like the waves. If only I could cross the river and proceed north, I'd find the Liberation Army. I'd join them; we'd fight southward, cross the Yangtze again to liberate the south, liberate my home village. . . .

I took out my last bit of food and was eating it when suddenly I heard quick footsteps from the bank and voices of men chasing someone. I stood up to look. A young man was running in my direction, chased by four Kuomintang soldiers. The soldiers were shouting, "Stop him!" When the youth came near, he looked at me with imploring eyes. I stepped aside to let him pass, but the soldiers kept on chasing him, and when they had almost overtaken him I heard a splash. He had leapt into the river! For a few seconds he rose and fell in the rolling waves, then a few gun shots were fired by the soldiers and the young man disappeared entirely.

The incident infuriated me. And, wouldn't they be after me too? I was going away when I heard someone behind me calling, "Catch this one!" Realizing they meant me, I ran for all I was worth, but only to collide with a dozen or more Kuomintang soldiers coming from the opposite direction. They seized me and took me to Goat's Horn Ferry.

On a ferry boat were six youths tied together in a row. I was taken aboard the boat and, with my hands tied behind my back, became the seventh. Two of the soldiers were left to guard us while the rest went off to eat. The two left behind were not happy about it, and stood to one side of the boat, looking glum.

I learned from the six youths that they were all press-ganged by the Kuomintang soldiers. There had been another who had gotten away — the one who jumped into the river and was shot dead.

I had fled Yao Pond Village to escape being dragged away as cannon-fodder. And here I was, bound up and heading for the same fate! Oh, Yangtze River, what pain and hatred you carry as you roll eastward! Was I to be captured so easily? No, I must not! I looked at the other six. Hatred and vexation were written plainly on their faces. Then I looked at the two guards, one standing near the prow of the boat and the other sitting some distance away. Both looked gloomy. Night was falling on the river, and there were few people on the quay. I was thinking of a way to escape. "Say," I called out to the guard standing near the prow, "are you taking us across?"

"Yes," answered the soldier laconically.

"When?"

"I don't know."

"Give me some water to drink," I said then.

"So much bother!" The soldier picked up a bowl, half filled it with water, and walked over to me. "Drink!" he said.

After I had taken a few swallows I intentionally knocked the bowl out of his hand with my head. It fell in several pieces. The soldier muttered a few curses, then ambled back to his place near the prow of the boat.

I looked at the other guard. He appeared to be dozing off, so I nudged the young man tied next to me and gave him a knowing look. He understood. We stooped together and each picked up a piece of the broken bowl. I whispered, "Cut!" and he sawed away at the cord that bound me. When my hands were freed, I helped to cut him free. The other five soon saw what we were doing and moved closer to us. The darkness and our own quietness protected us from the soldiers' attention. Keeping my hands behind my back, I motioned to the youth next

to me to knock out the dozing guard, while I'd give the other the same treatment. We closed in on them, and the dozing one was soon floundering about in the river, while the other was relieved of his gun. When he started running I ordered, "Don't move! If you run, I'll shoot!" When he saw his own gun aimed at him, he obediently halted.

The other five youths were all freed, ran ashore and soon disappeared. "You can go now," I said to the soldier, who was still standing there woodenly. And he scrambled ashore as fast as he could.

I found my small bundle and tied it round my waist. It would be difficult to carry a gun while swimming across the river, and further, carrying a gun on my journey north-ward would surely draw attention and arouse suspicion. So I reluctantly threw it into the river. Now I was ready to swim across the Yangtze! I plunged into the surging water and was soon rising and falling with the waves. I had only one thought: I must make it!

I was quite far out before I heard voices from the bank, and then two shots. I laughed, for I had got beyond them!

I swam and swam, but still there was no sign of the opposite bank. It was spring, and the water was cold. I didn't feel it at first in my anxiety to cross the river. But my arms and legs were now becoming numb. Suddenly a wind rose, and the waves swept me down river. Swimming now was very difficult, and I was exhausted. I felt attacked on all sides by the wind and waves, hunger and fatigue. Everything was enveloped in darkness. I had no idea how far I was from the opposite bank. But

I was not afraid or disheartened; I was sure I'd make it. Once I was north of the river, I would find the Liberation Army and avenge the poor for the wrongs done them. The North Star was exceptionally bright that night; it would continue leading me on my journey. Once again I gained strength and hope.

Swimming became more and more difficult, and sometimes I just floated, letting the waves carry me forward, then again exerting effort. I don't know how long I was in the water, but finally I heard dogs barking and knew I'd reached the northern shore!

I climbed out of the water utterly exhausted and fell flat on the bank. But I mustn't lie there, wet and shivering with cold. I mustn't get sick, or I wouldn't be able to go on looking for the Liberation Army! What was that? A fire? Sure enough, not far away was the glow of a campfire. I struggled to my feet and walked towards the glow.

Two old fishermen were cooking a meal by the river bank and looked surprised to see me. "I fell into the river," I explained. "Please let me dry off by your fire." The two old men looked me over from head to foot, but did not refuse my request. I squatted down before the fire to dry my clothes.

"You're not from these parts, are you?" one of them asked, likely noticing my dialect.

"No," I answered, "I'm from south of the river."

"You swam across?" the other joined in. "What made you take such chances?"

These two old men talked like poor folks, so I said right out, "I escaped from the pressgang."

"You did right. Even dying in the river is better than being conscripted into that kind of army!" the old fishermen sympathized.

We talked on, and when I found that these men had nothing but hatred for the Kuomintang army, I became bold enough to ask, "Where can I find the Liberation Army?"

"Continue north, and you'll find them." The two old men seemed to understand me. "Where there's fighting, there you'll find the Liberation Army," they said.

They were right! At dawn the next day, with these words in mind, I bade the two old fishermen goodbye and headed for "where there's fighting."

I inquired on the way and finally came to a place at the foot of Big Green Mountain where gunshots could easily be heard. An old woman carrying a basket came in the opposite direction. "Don't go any farther, there's fighting over there!" She was very kind to tell me so — and I thanked her for pointing out for me the very place I wanted to go. Kuomintang soldiers were straggling to this place in disorderly retreat. I took a detour uphill and hid in a cave.

Soon I heard a commotion, the noise of men and vehicles. I left the cave and climbed a hill from where I saw in the fields and on the roads below droves of Kuomintang soldiers who had apparently retreated there and begun to dig in. I counted more than thirty of them coming up the mountain. It was impossible to go back to the cave now, so I climbed higher and took shelter in a hole on the hill top. Some hundred metres from me they put up three machine-guns, and one directly below me. I had it all figured out — if any Kuomintang soldier came up and found me, I'd fight him and, as a last resort, take him down the precipice with me!

I could hear intense firing in the distance. How I wished I was there fighting together with the Liberation Army! Soon the shooting came nearer. Bullets flew overhead and some clattered on the rocks. Dusk was falling, and I could see the flashes of gunfire now in the darkness. Our own army could not be far away!

"Charge! Charge!" The sound came from the north. The enemy at the foot of the mountain was utterly routed. The three machine-guns above went frantically into action. I came out of the hole and, picking up some large rocks, threw them down on the machine-gun below me. A few more rocks aimed at the other machine-guns and the firing stopped, the enemy soldiers manning them taking to their heels without even looking to see what had happened.

The machine-guns were silenced. Now I could see many Liberation Army men dashing with fixed bayonets into the enemy ranks. I went after one of the machine-guns left by the enemy and wanted to dash with it into their ranks too, but didn't know how to use the gun. Then Liberation Army men came in force up the mountain, and one of them asked me, "Was it you who knocked out the enemy machine-guns?"

"Yes," I answered. "And here's one of them," I added, handing him the weapon.

He took it and shook my hand warmly. "Where did you come from?" he asked.

"From Kiangsi, looking for the Liberation Army."

Two more Liberation Army men came up, and the one who had been talking to me told the elder of these two, who, I learned later, was a political instructor, that it was I who helped to silence the enemy machine-guns, and that I had come from Kiangsi to find the Liberation Army.

"From Kiangsi?" The instructor came over and looked at me closely. Only then did I notice the red star that he and the other Liberation Army men wore on their caps! This was the Army I had been longing for every day, every hour! I took the political instructor's hands and said excitedly, "I came all the way from Kiangsi to find you. My father joined the Red Army and went on the Long March in 1934. . . ."

"You are our very own people!" said the political instructor to me warmly. "You must have had a very long and difficult journey."

"Yes, I have walked and swum to get here. . . ." I really could not tell how long I had been on the way, or how many hardships I had suffered.

The political instructor looked at the machine-gun. "You are very brave," said he, patting my shoulder. "What is your name?"

"Pan Chen-shan."

"Well, Comrade Pan Chen-shan." This was the first time I had ever been addressed as "comrade," and my heart warmed at the sound of it! Then, turning to the comrade beside him, the political instructor continued, "Young Wang, take Comrade Pan Chen-shan to battalion headquarters to rest."

"Oh, no," I put in, "I don't want to rest. Give me a gun so I can fight together with the comrades to wipe out the enemy."

"You'd better rest for a while," the political instructor advised. "There will be plenty of battles for you to fight.

When this one is over, we'll have a long talk." And with that he walked briskly away.

"Come on, let's go to battalion headquarters," urged Young Wang in a most warm-hearted manner.

The battle ended the next morning, and the comrades were busy sorting out the booty. I followed them around, trying my best to help. I was very excited and happy to be sharing in their joy of victory!

Our political instructor came to battalion headquarters that evening and said to me, "Comrade Pan Chen-shan, our division commander wants to see you."

"The division commander wants to see me?" I quickly took my mother's jacket and my father's red star out of my bundle.

"Come on, I'll go with you." As we walked through the village, the political instructor told me that he had spoken about me in the regiment and that the regiment reported to the division. And now the division commander wanted to see me! Soon the political instructor led me to a big courtyard with Liberation Army men in all the rooms. There were telephones in every room, and the comrades seemed very busy. We went into a north room. The political instructor saluted the leading comrade, who was making pencil marks on a map. "Division Commander, Comrade Pan Chen-shan is here," he said. Then turning to me, he added, "This is our division commander."

I bowed.

"Sit down," the division commander said. Then, putting down his pencil, he poured me a glass of water.

The political instructor saluted the division commander and left.

"Where is your home, Comrade Young Pan?" the division commander asked me with concern.

"In Willow Brook, Kiangsi."

"I see," the division commander nodded. "I hear you've come to look for your father?"

"Yes. My father joined the Long March in 1934. I have looked for him all these years, but never found him. When I heard there was fighting here, I walked in this direction."

"To join in an action as soon as you reach here —you're a brave boy," the division commander commended me. "How many are there in your family?"

"In my family. . . ." A lump came to my throat. "There *was* my mother when my father left. Later, my mother laid down her life." I unfolded the jacket. "This is the jacket my mother left me, and this is the red star father gave me to keep," I said.

The division commander took over my two treasures and looked at them as if they were his treasures too. He put the jacket on the table and then, holding the red star in his hand, commented, "Yes, this is the red star we wore at that time. The folks have kept them and continue the struggle." He walked to the window, which faced south, opened it and looked out. When he turned back, his eyes lighted up.

"Division Commander, you. . . ?"

"My surname is Chung. I'm from Hunan. I was in the Red Army on the Long March, too, in 1934." Placing the red star on top of the jacket, he continued, "I'm very

glad to see you. I feel proud of the Red Army that went on the Long March, and of their family members. Chairman Mao teaches us: **Wherever there is struggle there is sacrifice.** Our Red Army numbered hundreds of thousands, and they all left their families behind in their home villages. These family members have made sacrifices for the revolution. But their sacrifices were not made in vain. Don't you see that half of the country has already been liberated?" Pride resounded in the division commander's voice as he continued, "And we shall liberate the whole country! Now, listen to what Chairman Mao teaches us: **The Chinese people are suffering; it is our duty to save them and we must exert ourselves in struggle.**"

I was deeply moved, realizing that there were still many people living under oppression and, just as I was up to now, leading a miserable life. **". . . It is our duty to save them and we must exert ourselves in struggle."** How clear was Chairman Mao's teaching in my mind! "Commander," I said, "give me a gun, I want to go and fight the White guards!"

"Good! You ought to be a fighter and fight with a gun." The division commander went to the telephone. "Give me First Battalion. Hello! Is this Political Instructor Li? Come and take Comrade Pan Chen-shan to your battalion and enlist him into one of your companies." Putting down the receiver, he turned round and said to me, "Comrade Pan Chen-shan, you are a child of the Red Army; you must do your best to be a good fighter. We'll try to locate your father, and also Comrade Yao Hai-chuan."

I was happy beyond words. The day that I had been looking forward to had finally arrived! I dressed in the army uniform with a gun slung over my shoulder and a bright red star on my cap. How proud I felt! From now on I would be an armed revolutionary fighter and join in the actions together with the comrades.

The years of war sped past. . . . Life was so tense, so packed with events. Two years of fighting in the Liberation Army went by in a flash, and we had fought our way back across the Yangtze. With the momentum of a thunderbolt, our army swept back all the remnant Kuomintang forces.

Reared on the field of battle and educated and helped by my army commanders and comrades, I took my vow under the red flag and became a member of the glorious

Chinese Communist Party. And when our unit advanced on Kiangsi, I was appointed the leader of a scout squad.

After the counties near my home were liberated, our division encamped near a town. While there, Division Commander Chung sent for me.

"Comrade Pan Chen-shan," he said, "we've been so busy fighting we haven't managed to get news of your father. Now we've fought back to your home. Your village has been liberated. Go and have a look around."

I replied, "But I want to go south with our unit till the whole of China is liberated."

"Go home and have a look," insisted the division commander. "We're going to spend some time resting and regrouping here. Go back and see if there's any news of your father."

"I don't want to miss an action by going home."

"Yours is a special case," explained the division commander. "The political commissar and I, as well as your company cadres, all approve of your going."

Very moved, I saluted the division commander and expressed my gratitude for the Party's concern. "I'll go home for a look, but I'll come straight back," I promised.

X

Fifteen years had passed since my father left on the Long March in 1934. I, a child of seven then, had grown into a youth of twenty-two and a Liberation Army fighter. In the fifteen years I had escaped the enemy's clutches

127

many times. The hardships I experienced had enabled me to weather great storm and stress.

The Party and Chairman Mao had given me leadership and militant strength; the revolutionary people had reared me. Without the solicitude of the Party, the care of Uncle Sung and of Uncle Yao, the day I had longed for through those years could never have arrived. Now, on my way back on home leave, I wanted to stop at Yao Pond first to see Uncle Yao and his family.

The sun was setting and the mountains around were lovely in pink evening clouds. Yao Pond looked much more beautiful than when I left it. . . . Now, in my Liberation Army uniform, I attracted the villagers' attention, and when they recognized who I was, they all approached to greet me. Several children ran to Uncle Yao's home to tell the news, shouting as they ran, "Chen-shan has joined the P.L.A. and now he's back!"

I met Aunt and Uncle Yao, who came out to meet me. When I saluted, Uncle looked as if he could not believe his eyes, but soon cried out with joy, "So it's you, Chen-shan! You are a P.L.A. fighter now!" He grasped my hands and held them tightly. Aunt Yao was overjoyed.

"Why didn't you write?" said Uncle Yao.

"We were too busy fighting!" I replied. "Besides, my letters might not have reached you."

"Seen your father?"

"No." I shook my head. "Has Brother Hai-chuan written?"

"Oh, yes!" Aunt Yao put in. "And Hsiao-hung has gone to see him."

The news made me very happy.

"Let's go home and talk." I nodded to the villagers around me and went inside with Uncle, while Aunty began to prepare the meal.

When the meal was over, we talked far into the night. I told them how I had followed the sound of gunfire and found the Liberation Army, how I joined in the fighting, and how the army commanders tried to find news of my father and of Hai-chuan.

"Now that you're back, stay a while," said Aunt Yao.

"I can't. Fighting's still going on; the Kuomintang reactionaries aren't completely wiped out yet. Tomorrow I go to Willow Brook, and then back to our unit."

"Right. You mustn't stay away from the fighting."

After breakfast the next morning, Uncle and Aunt saw me to the edge of the village where, with brisk steps, I proceeded to Willow Brook.

The route to Willow Brook took me through the county seat, and I went to the rice shop where I had been apprenticed, to see Liu Lai-tzu. We were so happy to see each other again! He hoisted me up and looked at me closely. "So you're a P.L.A. man now! Tell me, how did you get away that day? Let's go to my room. Tell me all about it!"

I asked him why he was still there now that the county was liberated, and he answered, "I didn't want to stay, but the Federation of Industry and Commerce and the

Trade Union asked me to. There'll be struggles later in which I can take part."

"Right. There must be struggles. These blood-suckers — the bosses of the past — will they behave? Sharp struggles are still ahead!" I said.

We talked about many things till lunch time, when Liu Lai-tzu took me to a small restaurant to eat, then, after the meal, saw me off to the highway. I gripped his hand and said, "Don't forget how we poor people suffered in the past, how the bosses persecuted us. We'll have to wage hard struggles against them."

"I won't forget," Liu assured me.

And so we parted. Looking back at this former poor apprentice, I was sure he would struggle courageously against oppressors who were not reconciled to their defeat.

I headed for Willow Brook and reached home at dusk. Dear Willow Brook! I'd been away from my home village for fifteen years. As I drew near, I could feel my heart pounding and intuitively slowed my steps.

I went first to the end of the village, to the great tree where my mother died. It was already dark, but I seemed to see my mother there, and I wished I could say to her, "Ma, your son has come back!"

I stood under the tree for quite a while, hatred in my heart and longing to settle old scores with Hu Han-san. There were few people about in the village, and I wondered why it was so quiet tonight.

The cottage where I had lived had a light inside. The door was ajar, so I walked in and looked around. Nobody was there. Few traces were left of the home I had left fifteen years ago. I was turning to leave when a young man appeared.

"Who are you looking for, comrade?" he asked.

"I used to live in this village," I told him. "My name's Pan Chen-shan."

"Winter Boy!" and he bounded forward to take my arm. "I'm Sprig."

131

I gripped his hand tightly and exclaimed, "Well, we've both changed."

"We certainly have," said Sprig. "Meeting anywhere else, we wouldn't have recognized each other. Where have you been all these years? And when did you join the army?"

"That's a long story; it'll keep," I answered. "First, tell me, have you arrested Hu Han-san?"

"Not yet. He's a wily old fox. As soon as the P.L.A. came, he fled with his son to Rear Mountain. We've searched several times but haven't found them yet."

"We mustn't let him get away!" I put in quickly.

"We won't," Sprig said confidently. "A P.L.A. unit arrived this afternoon to help us capture him and the whole village is out, guarding every path up the mountain. He won't get away again!"

So that was why the village was deserted!

As we were talking, a shot rang out on Rear Mountain. "Gunfire!" I exclaimed. "I'm off."

"Here, take my broadsword," said Sprig, and I hurried to Rear Mountain, too.

It was pitch dark by now, but torches all over Rear Mountain made the place bright. As I entered a defile leading to it, a deep voice challenged, "Who goes there?" It came from behind a big crag.

"Pan Chen-shan."

"Who?" It sounded like the familiar voice of Uncle Sung.

"It's me, Winter Boy, Uncle," I answered.

"Who?" The man approached me. "Is it really you, Winter Boy?"

Uncle Sung took my hand. "So you're alive and well, my boy! And a soldier in the P.L.A.!"

"When did you get out of jail, Uncle?" I asked.

"I was locked up for several months. But that autumn Secretary Wu and his guerrillas raided the prison and let us out. Since then I've been fighting with the guerrillas."

"Is Secretary Wu here?"

"He's gone to the provincial capital, but he'll be back tomorrow."

Another shot rang out not far away. "Duck behind this rock," said Uncle Sung, and both of us took cover.

There was a second shot, then a figure appeared.

"Who goes there?" challenged Uncle Sung.

Whoever it was didn't answer, but dived into a clump of bamboo.

I went after the dark figure, followed close behind by Uncle Sung and some young village lads. We searched the bamboo grove, but our quarry had disappeared. Then I noticed in the beam of Uncle Sung's flashlight some trampled grass and footprints leading to a tumbledown wall. We rushed over to the courtyard there and I chucked a stone into it — not a sound. I vaulted onto the wall and, in that split second, saw someone climb out on the west side.

133

"Halt!" I shouted.

But whoever it was had gone.

When I jumped down from the wall, a bullet flew by my ear and from the flash I saw that the gunman was close at hand. "Where are you going?" I demanded, then charged with the sword. The first stroke missed, and a bullet grazed my arm. The flashlight beam suddenly lit up my adversary's face, and he dodged. I flew at him, striking the hand holding the gun. He shrieked and dropped the weapon.

Covering the gun with one foot, I looked at the cringing figure spotlighted by the flashlight beam. He was dressed like a peasant and had on a tattered felt hat.

"Head up!" ordered Uncle Sung.

The man refused, so I went up to him. But before I could see who it was, he pounced on me and tried to grab the broadsword out of my hand. I quickly drew the sword back through his hands.

I knocked his felt hat off. He looked up and I saw his face. It was Hu Han-san!

The hatred of a lifetime flared in my heart when I saw my old enemy. I roared at him, "Open your eyes, Hu Han-san, and see who's here!"

Hu glanced up at me and started shaking, then collapsed on the ground like a heap of soft mud.

Someone called out, "Look! They've captured Hu Han-san's son too." A crowd of people gathered around the prostrate figure of Hu Han-san, their flaming torches

134

turning the night as bright as day. I picked Hu Han-san from the ground and said to him in a loud and stern voice, "You owe the people a debt of blood, and the people are going to try you."

The capture of Hu Han-san cheered the people greatly. The request for a public trial was immediately granted by the higher authorities.

On the day of the public trial, we improvised a platform beneath the tree where my mother had died by the hand of Hu Han-san. Here, the people would try the murderer of many a revolutionary fighter.

Just before the public trial began, Uncle Sung pointed to a group of people on the road and asked, "Do you recognize someone there?"

It was Secretary Wu. I ran to him joyfully, calling, "Brother Wu! Do you know me?"

Secretary Wu looked at me closely. "So it's you, Winter Boy. You've come back a soldier in the P.L.A.!" He was very happy, too, to see me.

"All these years I've been trying to get news of you," I said.

"And we looked for you everywhere after you ran away from the rice shop," Secretary Wu rejoined.

"If it were not for Uncle Yao, I don't know how I'd have escaped from the clutches of the enemy."

"A seedling of the revolution will take root anywhere," was Brother Wu's comment. "The enemy can never wipe us out. Look at that specimen." Secretary Wu pointed at Hu Han-san on the improvised platform. "He and his sort are like grasshoppers in autumn — a few more jumps out of them and they're finished."

"The end of all enemies of the people," I put in.

"Let me tell you some good news," Secretary Wu went on. "We've received a letter from your father."

"Have you found my father at last?" I could hardly believe my ears. "Where is he?"

"In Tsinan." Secretary Wu took a letter out of his pocket. "He is now a deputy division commander."

My father! A man of medium height and sturdy build, large eyes flashing beneath the peak of an octagonal cap with a red star, a broadsword with a pennant of red silk on his back and a twenty-round Mauser pistol at his hip — this was the picture I had in my mind's eye of my father, an ordinary peasant who had been forced by oppression to make revolution and was now charged with the responsibility of commanding a whole division of the revolutionary troops.

"He asks for news of your mother and you. He'd like for you to go to Tsinan," Secretary Wu added.

"Mother!" I looked towards that big tree. If only my mother could see the red flags flying in our liberated village! See them by the tree where she laid down her life! If she could hear the songs of victory ringing in the air!

The public trial lasted the whole morning. Hu Hansan was sentenced to death, the sentence to be carried out immediately.

When old friends and kinsmen met again, how happy the meeting in this hour of victory! There was so much to tell! Brother Wu, Uncle Sung, Sprig and some other friends came to my old home and stayed chatting till after midnight.

After they had gone I sat down by the oil lamp, debating whether to go to Tsinan to see my father. I opened the bundle I had brought with me to have another look at my mother's jacket and the red star. Suddenly I remembered the bullet, and wondered if it was still under the pomegranate tree where mother had buried it.

I found a hoe and, taking a lantern, dug up the earth at the foot of the tree and searched through it till at last I found the bullet. It had lain buried there for fifteen years! How naively I had thought as a child: Dad's gone to fight the White guards today; tomorrow he'll come back victorious. I little realized at the time that this was an earth-shaking struggle in which the exploited classes were fighting to overthrow the ruling reactionaries, that the course of such a struggle could neither be short nor smooth. Holding the bullet in my hand, I recalled what Dad had said: "Remember that when you grow up, if any of those White guards are still around, you must go on fighting them." Now I had grown up, but not all the White guards had been wiped out. Of course I longed to see my father again, but if he knew that I was now a P.L.A. fighter, he surely would not hesitate to order me to the front. So I went back inside, took stationery from my pack and, by the light of the oil lamp, and with the bright red star on the table, wrote my father the following letter:

Dear Dad,

Your letter addressed to mother and me has been received. But mother will never be able to see it as she gave her life for the cause of the revolution fourteen years ago! Mother was a fine Communist, though she had been a Party member for only two days when she met her death. Her heroic image remains with us through the years.

After you left, mother never stopped struggling against the enemy, and was steeled in the fight. She went back to the village to mobilize the masses, and was seized while sheltering a comrade. The enemy could get nothing out of her, so they strung her up on the big tree at the east end of the village and built a fire beneath the tree. . . . She died a heroine.

Events in my childhood are still vivid in my memory. I need only to close my eyes and see you again, Dad. I'll never forget what you said to me when you gave me that blood-stained bullet: Fight the hated White guards when you grow up. I'll never forget that you gave the last of the pain-killer to another wounded Red Army soldier when you yourself needed it badly. You've taught me to love our comrades and our class brothers. I've finished reading the Lenin primary school textbook you gave me, Dad. I didn't study it in the Lenin primary school, but in the home of a revolutionary, an old man who lived in a thatched hut. The struggle we were engaged in at the time made me understand the text better. And I still have that red star you gave me, Dad. I don't know how many times I've looked at it! Each time I've felt very close to you. It went with me when I followed the North Star at night towards Yenan, when I swam the turbulent Yangtze in search of the Liberation Army. For fifteen years I've carried this red star with me. It has given me confidence, hope and courage; it has encouraged me to follow in your footsteps to live and persist in the struggle. I send the red star back to you, this time to remind you of me. Fifteen years! The red star is still as bright as ever.

After mother died, I stayed with Brother Wu and the guerrillas for a time. Then I was taken in by Uncle Sung, and later by Uncle Yao. All these years it's been the people who have brought me up.

My parents gave me birth; the people brought me up; the Party educates me and guides me forward. I have made my pledge under the red flag and am now a member of the Chinese Communist Party. I shall fight for the oppressed and exploited, to break the chains of the old world. I shall try to be a true Communist!

Mother once said, "Chairman Mao is our very best leader." She said it when she heard that Chairman Mao's leadership had been established at the Tsunyi Conference way back in 1935. How true her words are! Our victories today are all due to Chairman Mao's leadership. Dad, if you see Chairman Mao, please convey to him mother's and my boundless proletarian love for him!

I've been a soldier in the P.L.A. for two years now. You ask me to go to Tsinan to see you, but I don't plan to do that just now, as I want to return to the front immediately. When the whole country is liberated, I'll go to see you. I don't think that day is too far off.

Mother left me a jacket which I have kept these fifteen years. I'm sending it to you together with the red star. It'll remind you of mother, who was a staunch fighter till the very day of her martyrdom.

It's already dawn and I'm leaving for my unit. I'll write again from there.

With a revolutionary salute,

> Your son,
> Chen-shan (Winter Boy)

I blew out the lamp, folded my letter and put it in an envelope. Then I took out needle and thread to sew my mother's jacket and the red star into a small package. Secretary Wu and Uncle Sung appeared at the door.

"I'm not going to Tsinan just now," I announced.

When Uncle Sung asked why, I explained, "I'm going to rejoin my unit. When the whole country is liberated. . . ."

"Father and son will be reunited!" Secretary Wu completed the sentence for me.

With a laugh I nodded and asked him to post my letter and package to Tsinan for me. With deep emotion he accepted my request.

After breakfast I took leave of the villagers and my old home. I was on the march again, on my way to new battles.

闪闪的红星

李心田著　王维新插图

＊

外文出版社出版（北京）
1974年（34开）第一版
编号：（英）10050—797
00080
10—E—1325P